# SCIENCE AND HYPOTHESIS

# SCIENCE
# AND HYPOTHESIS

BY

## H. POINCARÉ,

MEMBER OF THE INSTITUTE OF FRANCE.

WITH A PREFACE BY

## J. LARMOR, D.Sc., Sec. R.S.,

*Lucasian Professor of Mathematics in the University of Cambridge.*

# DOVER PUBLICATIONS, INC.

New Dover edition is
an unabridged republication of
the first English translation.

*Library of Congress Catalog Card Number: 53-13673*

Manufactured in the United States of America

Dover Publications, Inc.
180 Varick Street
New York 14, N. Y.

# CONTENTS.

## PART I.

### *NUMBER AND MAGNITUDE.*

### CHAPTER I.

### CHAPTER II.

## PART II.

### *SPACE.*

### CHAPTER III.

## CHAPTER IV.

# PART III.

## *FORCE.*

## CHAPTER VI.

# PART IV.

## *NATURE.*

## CHAPTER IX.

# TRANSLATOR'S NOTE.

THE translator wishes to express his indebtedness to Professor Larmor, for kindly consenting to introduce the author of *Science and Hypothesis* to English readers; to Dr. F. S. Macaulay and Mr. C. S. Jackson, M.A., who have read the whole of the proofs and have greatly helped by suggestions; also to Professor G. H. Bryan, F.R.S., who has read the proofs of Chapter VIII., and whose criticisms have been most valuable.

W. J. G.

*February* 1905.

# INTRODUCTION.

———•••———

It is to be hoped that, as a consequence of the present active scrutiny of our educational aims and methods, and of the resulting encouragement of the study of modern languages, we shall not remain, as a nation, so much isolated from ideas and tendencies in continental thought and literature as we have been in the past. As things are, however, the translation of this book is doubtless required; at any rate, it brings vividly before us an instructive point of view. Though some of M. Poincaré's chapters have been collected from well-known treatises written several years ago, and indeed are sometimes in detail not quite up to date, besides occasionally suggesting the suspicion that his views may possibly have been modified in the interval, yet their publication in a compact form has excited a warm welcome in this country.

It must be confessed that the English language

hardly lends itself as a perfect medium for the rendering of the delicate shades of suggestion and allusion characteristic of M. Poincaré's play around his subject; notwithstanding the excellence of the translation, loss in this respect is inevitable.

There has been of late a growing trend of opinion, prompted in part by general philosophical views, in the direction that the theoretical constructions of physical science are largely factitious, that instead of presenting a valid image of the relations of things on which further progress can be based, they are still little better than a mirage. The best method of abating this scepticism is to become acquainted with the real scope and modes of application of conceptions which, in the popular language of superficial exposition—and even in the unguarded and playful paradox of their authors, intended only for the instructed eye— often look bizarre enough. But much advantage will accrue if men of science become their own epistemologists, and show to the world by critical exposition in non-technical terms of the results and methods of their constructive work, that more than mere instinct is involved in it: the community has indeed a right to expect as much as this.

It would be hard to find any one better qualified for this kind of exposition, either from the profundity of his own mathematical achievements, or from the extent and freshness of his interest in the theories of physical science, than the author of this book. If an appreciation might be ventured on as regards the later chapters, they are, perhaps, intended to present the stern logical analyst quizzing the cultivator of physical ideas as to what he is driving at, and whither he expects to go, rather than any responsible attempt towards a settled confession of faith. Thus, when M. Poincaré allows himself for a moment to indulge in a process of evaporation of the Principle of Energy, he is content to sum up: "Eh bien, quelles que soient les notions nouvelles que les expériences futures nous donneront sur le monde, nous sommes sûrs d'avance qu'il y aura quelque chose qui demeurera constant et que nous pourrons appeler *énergie*" (p. 166), and to leave the matter there for his readers to think it out. Though hardly necessary in the original French, it may not now be superfluous to point out that independent reflection and criticism on the part of the reader are tacitly implied here as elsewhere.

An interesting passage is the one devoted to

Maxwell's theory of the functions of the æther, and the comparison of the close-knit theories of the classical French mathematical physicists with the somewhat loosely-connected *corpus* of ideas by which Maxwell, the interpreter and successor of Faraday, has (posthumously) recast the whole face of physical science. How many times has that theory been re-written since Maxwell's day? and yet how little has it been altered in essence, except by further developments in the problem of moving bodies, from the form in which he left it! If, as M. Poincaré remarks, the French instinct for precision and lucid demonstration sometimes finds itself ill at ease with physical theories of the British school, he as readily admits (pp. 223, 224), and indeed fully appreciates, the advantages on the other side. Our own mental philosophers have been shocked at the point of view indicated by the proposition hazarded by Laplace, that a sufficiently developed intelligence, if it were made acquainted with the positions and motions of the atoms at any instant, could predict all future history: no amount of demur suffices sometimes to persuade them that this is not a conception universally entertained in physical science. It was not so even in Laplace's own day. From the point of view of the study of the evolution

of the sciences, there are few episodes more
instructive than the collision between Laplace
and Young with regard to the theory of capillarity. The precise and intricate mathematical
analysis of Laplace, starting from fixed pre-
conceptions regarding atomic forces which were
to remain intact throughout the logical development of the argument, came into contrast with the
tentative, mobile intuitions of Young; yet the
latter was able to grasp, by sheer direct mental
force, the fruitful though partial analogies of this
recondite class of phenomena with more familiar
operations of nature, and to form a direct picture
of the way things interacted, such as could only
have been illustrated, quite possibly damaged or
obliterated, by premature effort to translate it
into elaborate analytical formulas. The *aperçus*
of Young were apparently devoid of all cogency
to Laplace; while Young expressed, doubtless in
too extreme a way, his sense of the inanity of the
array of mathematical logic of his rival. The
subsequent history involved the Nemesis that the
fabric of Laplace was taken down and recon-
structed in the next generation by Poisson; while
the modern cultivator of the subject turns, at any
rate in England, to neither of those expositions
for illumination, but rather finds in the partial

and succinct indications of Young the best start-ing-point for further effort.

It seems, however, hard to accept entirely the distinction suggested (p. 213) between the methods of cultivating theoretical physics in the two countries. To mention only two transcendent names which stand at the very front of two of the greatest developments of physical science of the last century, Carnot and Fresnel, their procedure was certainly not on the lines thus described. Possibly it is not devoid of significance that each of them attained his first effective recognition from the British school.

It may, in fact, be maintained that the part played by mechanical and such-like theories—analogies if you will—is an essential one. The reader of this book will appreciate that the human mind has need of many instruments of comparison and discovery besides the unrelenting logic of the infinitesimal calculus. The dynamical basis which underlies the objects of our most frequent ex-perience has now been systematised into a great calculus of exact thought, and traces of new real relationships may come out more vividly when considered in terms of our familiar acquaintance with dynamical systems than when formulated under the paler shadow of more analytical abstractions.  It is even possible for a constructive physicist to conduct his mental operations entirely by dynamical images, though Helmholtz, as well as our author, seems to class a predilection in this direction as a British trait.  A time arrives when, as in other subjects, ideas have crystallised out into distinctness; their exact verification and development then becomes a problem in mathematical physics.  But whether the mechanical analogies still survive, or new terms are now introduced devoid of all naïve mechanical bias, it matters essentially little.  The precise determination of the relations of things in the rational scheme of nature in which we find ourselves is the fundamental task, and for its fulfilment in any direction advantage has to be taken of our knowledge, even when only partial, of new aspects and types of relationship which may have become familiar perhaps in quite different fields.  Nor can it be forgotten that the most fruitful and fundamental conceptions of abstract pure mathematics itself have often been suggested from these mechanical ideas of flux and force, where the play of intuition is our most powerful guide.  The study of the historical evolution of physical theories is essential to the complete understanding of their import.  It is in the mental workshop of a Fresnel, a Kelvin, or a Helmholtz, that profound ideas of the deep things of Nature are struck out and assume form; when pondered over and paraphrased by philosophers we see them react on the conduct of life: it is the business of criticism to polish them gradually to the common measure of human understanding. Oppressed though we are with the necessity of being specialists, if we are to know anything thoroughly in these days of accumulated details, we may at any rate profitably study the historical evolution of knowledge over a field wider than our own.

The aspect of the subject which has here been dwelt on is that scientific progress, considered historically, is not a strictly logical process, and does not proceed by syllogisms. New ideas emerge dimly into intuition, come into consciousness from nobody knows where, and become the material on which the mind operates, forging them gradually into consistent doctrine, which can be welded on to existing domains of knowledge. But this process is never complete: a crude connection can always be pointed to by a logician as an indication of the imperfection of human constructions.

If intuition plays a part which is so important,

it is surely necessary that we should possess a firm grasp of its limitations. In M. Poincaré's earlier chapters the reader can gain very pleasantly a vivid idea of the various and highly complicated ways of docketing our perceptions of the relations of external things, all equally valid, that were open to the human race to develop. Strange to say, they never tried any of them; and, satisfied with the very remarkable practical fitness of the scheme of geometry and dynamics that came naturally to hand, did not consciously trouble themselves about the possible existence of others until recently. Still more recently has it been found that the good Bishop Berkeley's logical jibes against the Newtonian ideas of fluxions and limiting ratios cannot be adequately appeased in the rigorous mathematical conscience, until our apparent continuities are resolved mentally into discrete aggregates which we only partially apprehend. The irresistible impulse to atomize everything thus proves to be not merely a disease of the physicist; a deeper origin, in the nature of knowledge itself, is suggested.

Everywhere want of absolute, exact adaptation can be detected, if pains are taken, between the various constructions that result from our mental activity and the impressions which give rise to them. The bluntness of our unaided sensual perceptions, which are the source in part of the intuitions of the race, is well brought out in this connection by M. Poincaré. Is there real contradiction? Harmony usually proves to be recovered by shifting our attitude to the phenomena. All experience leads us to interpret the totality of things as a consistent cosmos—undergoing evolution, the naturalists will say—in the large-scale workings of which we are interested spectators and explorers, while of the inner relations and ramifications we only apprehend dim glimpses. When our formulation of experience is imperfect or even paradoxical, we learn to attribute the fault to our point of view, and to expect that future adaptation will put it right. But Truth resides in a deep well, and we shall never get to the bottom. Only, while deriving enjoyment and insight from M. Poincaré's Socratic exposition of the limitations of the human outlook on the universe, let us beware of counting limitation as imperfection, and drifting into an inadequate conception of the wonderful fabric of human knowledge.

J. LARMOR.

# AUTHOR'S PREFACE.

To the superficial observer scientific truth is un-assailable, the logic of science is infallible; and if scientific men sometimes make mistakes, it is because they have not understood the rules of the game. Mathematical truths are derived from a few self-evident propositions, by a chain of flawless reasonings; they are imposed not only on us, but on Nature itself. By them the Creator is fettered, as it were, and His choice is limited to a relatively small number of solutions. A few experiments, therefore, will be sufficient to enable us to determine what choice He has made. From each experiment a number of consequences will follow by a series of mathematical deductions, and in this way each of them will reveal to us a corner of the universe. This, to the minds of most people, and to students who are getting their first ideas of physics, is the origin of certainty in science. This is what they take to be the rôle of experiment and mathematics. And thus, too, it was understood a hundred years ago by many men of science who dreamed of constructing the world with the aid of the smallest possible amount of material borrowed from experiment.

But upon more mature reflection the position held by hypothesis was seen; it was recognised that it is as necessary to the experimenter as it is to the mathematician. And then the doubt arose if all these constructions are built on solid foundations. The conclusion was drawn that a breath would bring them to the ground. This sceptical attitude does not escape the charge of superficiality. To doubt everything or to believe everything are two equally convenient solutions; both dispense with the necessity of reflection.

Instead of a summary condemnation we should examine with the utmost care the rôle of hypothesis; we shall then recognise not only that it is necessary, but that in most cases it is legitimate. We shall also see that there are several kinds of hypotheses; that some are verifiable, and when once confirmed by experiment become truths of great fertility; that others may be useful to us in fixing our ideas; and finally, that others are hypotheses only in appearance, and reduce to definitions or to conventions in disguise. The latter are to be met with especially in mathematics and in the sciences to which it is applied. From them, indeed, the sciences derive their rigour; such conventions are the result of the unrestricted activity of the mind, which in this domain recognises no obstacle. For here the mind may affirm because it lays down its own laws; but let us clearly understand that while these laws are imposed on *our* science, which otherwise could not exist, they are not imposed on Nature. Are they then arbitrary? No; for if they were, they would not be fertile. Experience leaves us our freedom of choice, but it guides us by helping us to discern the most convenient path to follow. Our laws are therefore like those of an absolute monarch, who is wise and consults his council of state. Some people have been struck by this characteristic of free convention which may be recognised in certain fundamental principles of the sciences. Some have set no limits to their generalisations, and at the same time they have forgotten that there is a difference between liberty and the purely arbitrary. So that they are compelled to end in what is called *nominalism;* they have asked if the *savant* is not the dupe of his own definitions, and if the world he thinks he has discovered is not simply the creation of his own caprice.[1] Under these conditions science would retain its certanty, but would not attain its object, and would become powerless. Now, we daily see what science is doing for us. This could not be unless it taught us something about reality; the aim of science is not things themselves, as the dogmatists in their simplicity imagine, but the relations between things; outside those relations there is no reality knowable.

Such is the conclusion to which we are led; but to reach that conclusion we must pass in review the series of sciences from arithmetic and geometry to mechanics and experimental physics. What is the nature of mathematical reasoning? Is it really deductive, as is commonly supposed? Careful analysis shows us that it is nothing of the kind; that it participates to some extent in the nature of inductive reasoning, and for that reason it is fruitful. But none the less does it retain its character of absolute rigour; and this is what must first be shown.

When we know more of this instrument which is placed in the hands of the investigator by mathematics, we have then to analyse another fundamental idea, that of mathematical magni-

---

[1] Cf. M. le Roy: "Science et Philosophie," *Revue de Métaphysique et de Morale*, 1901.

tude.  Do we find it in nature, or have we ourselves introduced it?  And if the latter be the
case, are we not running a risk of coming to
incorrect conclusions all round?  Comparing the
rough data of our senses with that extremely complex and subtle conception which mathematicians
call magnitude, we are compelled to recognise a
divergence.  The framework into which we wish
to make everything fit is one of our own construction; but we did not construct it at random, we
constructed it by measurement so to speak; and
that is why we can fit the facts into it without
altering their essential qualities.

Space is another framework which we impose
on the world.  Whence are the first principles of
geometry derived?  Are they imposed on us by
logic?  Lobatschewsky, by inventing non-Euclidean geometries, has shown that this is not the case.
Is space revealed to us by our senses?  No; for
the space revealed to us by our senses is absolutely
different from the space of geometry.  Is geometry
derived from experience?  Careful discussion will
give the answer—no!  We therefore conclude that
the principles of geometry are only conventions;
but these conventions are not arbitrary, and if
transported into another world (which I shall
call the non-Euclidean world, and which I shall

endeavour to describe), we shall find ourselves compelled to adopt more of them.

In mechanics we shall be led to analogous con-clusions, and we shall see that the principles of this science, although more directly based on experience, still share the conventional character of the geometrical postulates. So far, nominalism triumphs; but we now come to the physical sciences, properly so called, and here the scene changes. We meet with hypotheses of another kind, and we fully grasp how fruitful they are. No doubt at the outset theories seem unsound, and the history of science shows us how ephemeral they are; but they do not entirely perish, and of each of them some traces still remain. It is these traces which we must try to discover, because in them and in them alone is the true reality.

The method of the physical sciences is based upon the induction which leads us to expect the recurrence of a phenomenon when the circum-stances which give rise to it are repeated. If all the circumstances could be simultaneously re-produced, this principle could be fearlessly applied; but this never happens; some of the circumstances will always be missing. Are we absolutely certain that they are unimportant? Evidently not! It may be probable, but it cannot be rigorously certain.   Hence the importance of the rôle that is played in the physical sciences by the law of probability.   The calculus of probabilities is therefore not merely a recreation, or a guide to the baccarat player; and we must thoroughly examine the principles on which it is based.   In this connection I have but very incomplete results to lay before the reader, for the vague instinct which enables us to determine probability almost defies analysis.   After a study of the conditions under which the work of the physicist is carried on, I have thought it best to show him at work.   For this purpose I have taken instances from the history of optics and of electricity.   We shall thus see how the ideas of Fresnel and Maxwell took their rise, and what unconscious hypotheses were made by Ampère and the other founders of electro-dynamics.

# SCIENCE AND HYPOTHESIS.

---◆---

## PART I.

### *NUMBER AND MAGNITUDE.*

## CHAPTER I.

### ON THE NATURE OF MATHEMATICAL REASONING.

### I.

THE very possibility of mathematical science seems
an insoluble contradiction. If this science is only
deductive in appearance, from whence is derived
that perfect rigour which is challenged by none?
If, on the contrary, all the propositions which it
enunciates may be derived in order by the rules
of formal logic, how is it that mathematics is
not reduced to a gigantic tautology? The syllogism can teach us nothing essentially new, and
if everything must spring from the principle of
identity, then everything should be capable of
being reduced to that principle. Are we then to
admit that the enunciations of all the theorems

with which so many volumes are filled, are only indirect ways of saying that A is A ?

No doubt we may refer back to axioms which are at the source of all these reasonings. If it is felt that they cannot be reduced to the principle of contradiction, if we decline to see in them any more than experimental facts which have no part or lot in mathematical necessity, there is still one resource left to us: we may class them among *à priori* synthetic views. But this is no solution of the difficulty—it is merely giving it a name; and even if the nature of the synthetic views had no longer for us any mystery, the contradiction would not have disappeared; it would have only been shirked. Syllogistic reasoning remains incapable of adding anything to the data that are given it; the data are reduced to axioms, and that is all we should find in the conclusions.

No theorem can be new unless a new axiom intervenes in its demonstration; reasoning can only give us immediately evident truths borrowed from direct intuition; it would only be an inter-mediary parasite. Should we not therefore have reason for asking if the syllogistic apparatus serves only to disguise what we have borrowed?

The contradiction will strike us the more if we open any book on mathematics; on every page the author announces his intention of generalising some proposition already known. Does the mathematical method proceed from the particular to the general, and, if so, how can it be called deductive?

Finally, if the science of number were merely analytical, or could be analytically derived from a few synthetic intuitions, it seems that a sufficiently powerful mind could with a single glance perceive all its truths; nay, one might even hope that some day a language would be invented simple enough for these truths to be made evident to any person of ordinary intelligence.

Even if these consequences are challenged, it must be granted that mathematical reasoning has of itself a kind of creative virtue, and is therefore to be distinguished from the syllogism. The difference must be profound. We shall not, for instance, find the key to the mystery in the frequent use of the rule by which the same uniform operation applied to two equal numbers will give identical results. All these modes of reasoning, whether or not reducible to the syllogism, properly so called, retain the analytical character, and *ipso facto*, lose their power.

## II.

The argument is an old one. Let us see how Leibnitz tried to show that two and two make four. I assume the number one to be defined, and also the operation $x + 1$—*i.e.*, the adding of unity to a given number $x$. These definitions, whatever they may be, do not enter into the subsequent reasoning. I next define the numbers 2, 3, 4 by the equalities:—

(1) $1 + 1 = 2$; (2) $2 + 1 = 3$; (3) $3 + 1 = 4$, and in

the same way I define the operation $x+2$ by the relation; (4) $x+2=(x+1)+1$.

Given this, we have :—

$$2+2=(2+1)+1 ; \quad \text{(def. 4).}$$
$$(2+1)+1=3+1 \quad \text{(def. 2).}$$
$$3+1=4 \quad \text{(def. 3).}$$

whence $2+2=4$                Q.E.D.

It cannot be denied that this reasoning is purely analytical. But if we ask a mathematician, he will reply: "This is not a demonstration properly so called; it is a verification." We have confined ourselves to bringing together one or other of two purely conventional definitions, and we have verified their identity; nothing new has been learned. *Verification* differs from proof precisely because it is analytical, and because it leads to nothing. It leads to nothing because the conclusion is nothing but the premisses translated into another language. A real proof, on the other hand, is fruitful, because the conclusion is in a sense more general than the premisses. The equality $2+2=4$ can be verified because it is particular. Each individual enunciation in mathematics may be always verified in the same way. But if mathematics could be reduced to a series of such verifications it would not be a science. A chess-player, for instance, does not create a science by winning a piece. There is no science but the science of the general. It may even be said that the object of the exact sciences is to dispense with these direct verifications.

## III.

Let us now see the geometer at work, and try to surprise some of his methods. The task is not without difficulty; it is not enough to open a book at random and to analyse any proof we may come across. First of all, geometry must be excluded, or the question becomes complicated by difficult problems relating to the rôle of the postulates, the nature and the origin of the idea of space. For analogous reasons we cannot avail ourselves of the infinitesimal calculus. We must seek mathematical thought where it has remained pure—*i.e.*, in Arithmetic. But we still have to choose; in the higher parts of the theory of numbers the primitive mathematical ideas have already undergone so profound an elaboration that it becomes difficult to analyse them.

It is therefore at the beginning of Arithmetic that we must expect to find the explanation we seek; but it happens that it is precisely in the proofs of the most elementary theorems that the authors of classic treatises have displayed the least precision and rigour. We may not impute this to them as a crime; they have obeyed a necessity. Beginners are not prepared for real mathematical rigour; they would see in it nothing but empty, tedious subtleties. It would be waste of time to try to make them more exacting; they have to pass rapidly and without stopping over the road which was trodden slowly by the founders of the science.

Why is so long a preparation necessary to habituate oneself to this perfect rigour, which it would seem should naturally be imposed on all minds? This is a logical and psychological problem which is well worthy of study. But we shall not dwell on it; it is foreign to our subject. All I wish to insist on is, that we shall fail in our purpose unless we reconstruct the proofs of the elementary theorems, and give them, not the rough form in which they are left so as not to weary the beginner, but the form which will satisfy the skilled geometer.

### DEFINITION OF ADDITION.

I assume that the operation $x + 1$ has been defined; it consists in adding the number 1 to a given number $x$. Whatever may be said of this definition, it does not enter into the subsequent reasoning.

We now have to define the operation $x + a$, which consists in adding the number $a$ to any given number $x$. Suppose that we have defined the operation $x + (a - 1)$; the operation $x + a$ will be defined by the equality: (1) $x + a = [x + (a - 1)] + 1$. We shall know what $x + a$ is when we know what $x + (a - 1)$ is, and as I have assumed that to start with we know what $x + 1$ is, we can define successively and "by recurrence" the operations $x + 2, x + 3$, etc. This definition deserves a moment's attention; it is of a particular nature which distinguishes it even at this stage from the purely logical definition; the equality (1), in fact, contains an infinite number of distinct definitions, each having only one meaning when we know the meaning of its predecessor.

## PROPERTIES OF ADDITION.

*Associative.*—I say that $a+(b+c)=(a+b)+c$; in fact, the theorem is true for $c=1$. It may then be written $a+(b+1)=(a+b)+1$; which, remembering the difference of notation, is nothing but the equality (1) by which I have just defined addition. Assume the theorem true for $c=\gamma$, I say that it will be true for $c=\gamma+1$. Let $(a+b)+\gamma=a+(b+\gamma)$, it follows that $[(a+b)+\gamma]+1=[a+(b+\gamma)]+1$; or by def. (1)— $(a+b)+(\gamma+1)=a+(b+\gamma+1)=a+[b+(\gamma+1)]$, which shows by a series of purely analytical deductions that the theorem is true for $\gamma+1$. Being true for $c=1$, we see that it is successively true for $c=2$, $c=3$, etc.

*Commutative.*—(1) I say that $a+1=1+a$. The theorem is evidently true for $a=1$; we can *verify* by purely analytical reasoning that if it is true for $a=\gamma$ it will be true for $a=\gamma+1$.[1] Now, it is true for $a=1$, and therefore is true for $a=2$, $a=3$, and so on. This is what is meant by saying that the proof is demonstrated " by recurrence."

(2) I say that $a+b=b+a$. The theorem has just

[1] For $(\gamma+1)+1=(1+\gamma)+1=1+(\gamma+1)$.—[TR.]

been shown to hold good for $b = 1$, and it may be verified analytically that if it is true for $b = \beta$, it will be true for $b = \beta + 1$. The proposition is thus established by recurrence.

## DEFINITION OF MULTIPLICATION.

We shall define multiplication by the equalities: (1) $a \times 1 = a$. (2) $a \times b = [a \times (b-1)] + a$. Both of these include an infinite number of definitions; having defined $a \times 1$, it enables us to define in succession $a \times 2$, $a \times 3$, and so on.

## PROPERTIES OF MULTIPLICATION.

*Distributive.*— I say that $(a+b) \times c = (a \times c) + (b \times c)$. We can verify analytically that the theorem is true for $c = 1$; then if it is true for $c = \gamma$, it will be true for $c = \gamma + 1$. The proposition is then proved by recurrence.

*Commutative.*—(1) I say that $a \times 1 = 1 \times a$. The theorem is obvious for $a = 1$. We can verify analytically that if it is true for $a = a$, it will be true for $a = a + 1$.

(2) I say that $a \times b = b \times a$. The theorem has just been proved for $b = 1$. We can verify analytically that if it be true for $b = \beta$ it will be true for $b = \beta + 1$.

## IV.

This monotonous series of reasonings may now be laid aside; but their very monotony brings vividly to light the process, which is uniform, and is met again at every step. The process is proof by recurrence. We first show that a theorem is true for $n=1$; we then show that if it is true for $n-1$ it is true for $n$, and we conclude that it is true for all integers. We have now seen how it may be used for the proof of the rules of addition and multiplication—that is to say, for the rules of the algebraical calculus. This calculus is an instrument of transformation which lends itself to many more different combinations than the simple syllogism; but it is still a purely analytical instrument, and is incapable of teaching us anything new. If mathematics had no other instrument, it would immediately be arrested in its development; but it has recourse anew to the same process—*i.e.*, to reasoning by recurrence, and it can continue its forward march. Then if we look carefully, we find this mode of reasoning at every step, either under the simple form which we have just given to it, or under a more or less modified form. It is therefore mathematical reasoning *par excellence*, and we must examine it closer.

## V.

The essential characteristic of reasoning by recurrence is that it contains, condensed, so to speak, in a single formula, an infinite number of syllogisms. We shall see this more clearly if we enunciate the syllogisms one after another. They follow one another, if one may use the expression, in a cascade. The following are the hypothetical syllogisms:—The theorem is true of the number 1. Now, if it is true of 1, it is true of 2; therefore it is true of 2.   Now, if it is true of 2, it is true of 3; hence it is true of 3, and so on.   We see that the conclusion of each syllogism serves as the minor of its successor.   Further, the majors of all our syllogisms may be reduced to a single form.   If the theorem is true of $n - 1$, it is true of $n$.

We see, then, that in reasoning by recurrence we confine ourselves to the enunciation of the minor of the first syllogism, and the general formula which contains as particular cases all the majors.   This unending series of syllogisms is thus reduced to a phrase of a few lines.

It is now easy to understand why every particular consequence of a theorem may, as I have above explained, be verified by purely analytical processes.   If, instead of proving that our theorem is true for all numbers, we only wish to show that it is true for the number 6 for instance, it will be enough to establish the first five syllogisms in our cascade.   We shall require 9 if we wish to prove it for the number 10; for a greater number we shall require more still; but however great the number may be we shall always reach it, and the analytical verification will always be possible. But however far we went we should never reach the general theorem applicable to all numbers, which alone is the object of science.   To reach it we should require an infinite number of syllogisms, and we should have to cross an abyss which the patience of the analyst, restricted to the resources of formal logic, will never succeed in crossing.

I asked at the outset why we cannot conceive of a mind powerful enough to see at a glance the whole body of mathematical truth.  The answer is now easy.  A chess-player can combine for four or five moves ahead; but, however extraordinary a player he may be, he cannot prepare for more than a finite number of moves.  If he applies his faculties to Arithmetic, he cannot conceive its general truths by direct intuition alone; to prove even the smallest theorem he must use reasoning by recurrence, for that is the only instrument which enables us to pass from the finite to the infinite. This instrument is always useful, for it enables us to leap over as many stages as we wish; it frees us from the necessity of long, tedious, and monotonous verifications which would rapidly become impracticable.  Then when we take in hand the general theorem it becomes indispensable, for otherwise we should ever be approaching the analytical verification without ever actually reaching it.  In this domain of Arithmetic we may think ourselves very far from the infinitesimal analysis, but the idea of mathematical infinity is already playing a preponderating part, and without it there would be no science at all, because there would be nothing general.

## VI.

The views upon which reasoning by recurrence is based may be exhibited in other forms; we may say, for instance, that in any finite collection of different integers there is always one which is smaller than any other. We may readily pass from one enunciation to another, and thus give ourselves the illusion of having proved that reasoning by recurrence is legitimate. But we shall always be brought to a full stop—we shall always come to an indemonstrable axiom, which will at bottom be but the proposition we had to prove translated into another language. We cannot therefore escape the conclusion that the rule of reasoning by recurrence is irreducible to the principle of contradiction. Nor can the rule come to us from experiment. Experiment may teach us that the rule is true for the first ten or the first hundred numbers, for instance; it will not bring us to the indefinite series of numbers, but only to a more or less long, but always limited, portion of the series.

Now, if that were all that is in question, the principle of contradiction would be sufficient, it would always enable us to develop as many syllogisms as we wished. It is only when it is a question of a single formula to embrace an infinite number of syllogisms that this principle breaks down, and there, too, experiment is powerless to aid. This rule, inaccessible to analytical proof and to experiment, is the exact type of the *à priori* synthetic intuition.   On the other hand, we cannot see in it a convention as in the case of the postulates of geometry.

Why then is this view imposed upon us with such an irresistible weight of evidence?   It is because it is only the affirmation of the power of the mind which knows it can conceive of the indefinite repetition of the same act, when the act is once possible.   The mind has a direct intuition of this power, and experiment can only be for it an opportunity of using it, and thereby of becoming conscious of it.

But it will be said, if the legitimacy of reasoning by recurrence cannot be established by experiment alone, is it so with experiment aided by induction? We see successively that a theorem is true of the number 1, of the number 2, of the number 3, and so on—the law is manifest, we say, and it is so on the same ground that every physical law is true which is based on a very large but limited number of observations.

It cannot escape our notice that here is a striking analogy with the usual processes of induction.   But an essential difference exists. Induction applied to the physical sciences is always uncertain, because it is based on the belief in a general order of the universe, an order which is external to us.   Mathematical induction —*i.e.*, proof by recurrence—is, on the contrary, necessarily imposed on us, because it is only the affirmation of a property of the mind itself.

## VII.

Mathematicians, as I have said before, always endeavour to generalise the propositions they have obtained. To seek no further example, we have just shown the equality, $a + 1 = 1 + a$, and we then used it to establish the equality, $a + b = b + a$, which is obviously more general. Mathematics may, therefore, like the other sciences, proceed from the particular to the general. This is a fact which might otherwise have appeared incomprehensible to us at the beginning of this study, but which has no longer anything mysterious about it, since we have ascertained the analogies between proof by recurrence and ordinary induction.

No doubt mathematical recurrent reasoning and physical inductive reasoning are based on different foundations, but they move in parallel lines and in the same direction—namely, from the particular to the general.

Let us examine the case a little more closely. To prove the equality $a + 2 = 2 + a \ldots \ldots (1)$, we need only apply the rule. $a + 1 = 1 + a$, twice, and write $a + 2 = a + 1 + 1 = 1 + a + 1 = 1 + 1 + a = 2 + a \ldots \ldots (2)$.

The equality thus deduced by purely analytical means is not, however, a simple particular case. It is something quite different. We may not therefore even say in the really analytical and deductive part of mathematical reasoning that we proceed from the general to the particular in the ordinary sense of the words. The two sides of the equality (2) are merely more complicated combinations than the two sides of the equality (1), and analysis only serves to separate the elements which enter into these combinations and to study their relations.

Mathematicians therefore proceed "by construction," they "construct" more complicated combinations. When they analyse these combinations, these aggregates, so to speak, into their primitive elements, they see the relations of the elements and deduce the relations of the aggregates themselves. The process is purely analytical, but it is not a passing from the general to the particular, for the aggregates obviously cannot be regarded as more particular than their elements.

Great importance has been rightly attached to this process of "construction," and some claim to see in it the necessary and sufficient condition of the progress of the exact sciences. Necessary, no doubt, but not sufficient! For a construction to be useful and not mere waste of mental effort, for it to serve as a stepping-stone to higher things, it must first of all possess a kind of unity enabling us to see something more than the juxtaposition of its elements. Or more accurately, there must be some advantage in considering the construction rather than the elements themselves. What can this advantage be? Why reason on a polygon, for instance, which is always decomposable into triangles, and not on elementary triangles? It is because there are properties of polygons of any number of sides, and they can be immediately applied to any particular kind of polygon. In most cases it is only after long efforts that those properties can be discovered, by directly studying the relations of elementary triangles. If the quadrilateral is anything more than the juxta-position of two triangles, it is because it is of the polygon type.

A construction only becomes interesting when it can be placed side by side with other analogous constructions for forming species of the same genus. To do this we must necessarily go back from the particular to the general, ascending one or more steps. The analytical process "by construction" does not compel us to descend, but it leaves us at the same level. We can only ascend by mathematical induction, for from it alone can we learn something new. Without the aid of this induction, which in certain respects differs from, but is as fruitful as, physical induction, construction would be powerless to create science.

Let me observe, in conclusion, that this induction is only possible if the same operation can be repeated indefinitely. That is why the theory of chess can never become a science, for the different moves of the same piece are limited and do not resemble each other.

# CHAPTER II.

## MATHEMATICAL MAGNITUDE AND EXPERIMENT.

If we want to know what the mathematicians mean by a continuum, it is useless to appeal to geometry. The geometer is always seeking, more or less, to represent to himself the figures he is studying, but his representations are only instruments to him; he uses space in his geometry just as he uses chalk; and further, too much importance must not be attached to accidents which are often nothing more than the whiteness of the chalk.

The pure analyst has not to dread this pitfall. He has disengaged mathematics from all extraneous elements, and he is in a position to answer our question:—"Tell me exactly what this continuum is, about which mathematicians reason." Many analysts who reflect on their art have already done so—M. Tannery, for instance, in his *Introduction à la théorie des Fonctions d'une variable.*

Let us start with the integers. Between any two consecutive sets, intercalate one or more intermediary sets, and then between these sets others again, and so on indefinitely. We thus get an unlimited number of terms, and these will be the numbers which we call fractional, rational, or commensurable. But this is not yet all; between these terms, which, be it marked, are already infinite in number, other terms are intercalated, and these are called irrational or incommensurable.

Before going any further, let me make a preliminary remark. The continuum thus conceived is no longer a collection of individuals arranged in a certain order, infinite in number, it is true, but external the one to the other. This is not the ordinary conception in which it is supposed that between the elements of the continuum exists an intimate connection making of it one whole, in which the point has no existence previous to the line, but the line does exist previous to the point. Multiplicity alone subsists, unity has disappeared —"the continuum is unity in multiplicity," according to the celebrated formula. The analysts have even less reason to define their continuum as they do, since it is always on this that they reason when they are particularly proud of their rigour. It is enough to warn the reader that the real mathematical continuum is quite different from that of the physicists and from that of the metaphysicians.

It may also be said, perhaps, that mathematicians who are contented with this definition are the dupes of words, that the nature of each of these sets should be precisely indicated, that it should be explained how they are to be intercalated, and that it should be shown how it is possible to do it. This, however, would be wrong; the only property of the sets which comes into the reasoning is that of preceding or succeeding these or those other sets; this alone should therefore intervene in the definition. So we need not concern ourselves with the manner in which the sets are intercalated, and no one will doubt the possibility of the operation if he only remembers that "possible" in the language of geometers simply means exempt from contradiction. But our definition is not yet complete, and we come back to it after this rather long digression.

*Definition of Incommensurables.*—The mathematicians of the Berlin school, and Kronecker in particular, have devoted themselves to constructing this continuous scale of irrational and fractional numbers without using any other materials than the integer. The mathematical continuum from this point of view would be a pure creation of the mind in which experiment would have no part.

The idea of rational number not seeming to present to them any difficulty, they have confined their attention mainly to defining incommensurable numbers. But before reproducing their definition here, I must make an observation that will allay the astonishment which this will not fail to provoke in readers who are but little familiar with the habits of geometers.

Mathematicians do not study objects, but the relations between objects; to them it is a matter of indifference if these objects are replaced by others, provided that the relations do not change. Matter does not engage their attention, they are interested by form alone.

If we did not remember it, we could hardly understand that Kronecker gives the name of incommensurable number to a simple symbol— that is to say, something very different from the idea we think we ought to have of a quantity which should be measurable and almost tangible.

Let us see now what is Kronecker's definition. Commensurable numbers may be divided into classes in an infinite number of ways, subject to the condition that any number whatever of the first class is greater than any number of the second. It may happen that among the numbers of the first class there is one which is smaller than all the rest; if, for instance, we arrange in the first class all the numbers greater than 2, and 2 itself, and in the second class all the numbers smaller than 2, it is clear that 2 will be the smallest of all the numbers of the first class. The number 2 may therefore be chosen as the symbol of this division.

It may happen, on the contrary, that in the second class there is one which is greater than all the rest. This is what takes place, for example, if the first class comprises all the numbers greater than 2, and if, in the second, are all the numbers less than 2, and 2 itself. Here again the number 2 might be chosen as the symbol of this division.

But it may equally well happen that we can find neither in the first class a number smaller than all the rest, nor in the second class a number greater than all the rest. Suppose, for instance, we place in the first class all the numbers whose squares are greater than 2, and in the second all the numbers whose squares are smaller than 2. We know that in neither of them is a number whose square is equal to 2. Evidently there will be in the first class no number which is smaller than all the rest, for however near the square of a number may be to 2, we can always find a commensurable whose square is still nearer to 2. From Kronecker's point of view, the incommensurable number $\sqrt{2}$ is nothing but the symbol of this particular method of division of commensurable numbers; and to each mode of repartition corresponds in this way a number, commensurable or not, which serves as a symbol. But to be satisfied with this would be to forget the origin of these symbols; it remains to explain how we have been led to attribute to them a kind of concrete existence, and on the other hand, does not the difficulty begin with fractions? Should we have the notion of these numbers if we did not previously know a matter which we conceive as infinitely divisible—*i.e.*, as a continuum?

*The Physical Continuum.*—We are next led to ask

if the idea of the mathematical continuum is not simply drawn from experiment.  If that be so, the rough data of experiment, which are our sensations, could be measured.  We might, indeed, be tempted to believe that this is so, for in recent times there has been an attempt to measure them, and a law has even been formulated, known as Fechner's law, according to which sensation is proportional to the logarithm of the stimulus.  But if we examine the experiments by which the endeavour has been made to establish this law, we shall be led to a diametrically opposite conclusion.  It has, for instance, been observed that a weight A of 10 grammes and a weight B of 11 grammes produced identical sensations, that the weight B could no longer be distinguished from a weight C of 12 grammes, but that the weight A was readily distinguished from the weight C.  Thus the rough results of the experiments may be expressed by the following relations: $A = B, B = C, A < C$, which may be regarded as the formula of the physical continuum.  But here is an intolerable disagreement with the law of contradiction, and the necessity of banishing this disagreement has compelled us to invent the mathematical continuum. We are therefore forced to conclude that this notion has been created entirely by the mind, but it is experiment that has provided the opportunity. We cannot believe that two quantities which are equal to a third are not equal to one another, and we are thus led to suppose that A is different from

B, and B from C, and that if we have not been aware of this, it is due to the imperfections of our senses.

*The Creation of the Mathematical Continuum: First Stage.*—So far it would suffice, in order to account for facts, to intercalate between A and B a small number of terms which would remain discrete. What happens now if we have recourse to some instrument to make up for the weakness of our senses? If, for example, we use a microscope? Such terms as A and B, which before were indistinguishable from one another, appear now to be distinct: but between A and B, which are distinct, is intercalated another new term D, which we can distinguish neither from A nor from B. Although we may use the most delicate methods, the rough results of our experiments will always present the characters of the physical continuum with the contradiction which is inherent in it. We only escape from it by incessantly intercalating new terms between the terms already distinguished, and this operation must be pursued indefinitely. We might conceive that it would be possible to stop if we could imagine an instrument powerful enough to decompose the physical continuum into discrete elements, just as the telescope resolves the Milky Way into stars. But this we cannot imagine; it is always with our senses that we use our instruments; it is with the eye that we observe the image magnified by the microscope, and this image must therefore always retain the characters of visual sensation, and therefore those of the physical continuum.

Nothing distinguishes a length directly observed from half that length doubled by the microscope. The whole is homogeneous to the part; and there is a fresh contradiction—or rather there would be one if the number of the terms were supposed to be finite; it is clear that the part containing less terms than the whole cannot be similar to the whole. The contradiction ceases as soon as the number of terms is regarded as infinite. There is nothing, for example, to prevent us from regarding the aggregate of integers as similar to the aggregate of even numbers, which is however only a part of it; in fact, to each integer corresponds another even number which is its double. But it is not only to escape this contradiction contained in the empiric data that the mind is led to create the concept of a continuum formed of an indefinite number of terms.

Here everything takes place just as in the series of the integers. We have the faculty of conceiving that a unit may be added to a collection of units. Thanks to experiment, we have had the opportunity of exercising this faculty and are conscious of it; but from this fact we feel that our power is unlimited, and that we can count indefinitely, although we have never had to count more than a finite number of objects. In the same way, as soon as we have intercalated terms between two consecutive terms of a series, we feel that this operation may be continued without limit, and that, so to speak, there is no intrinsic reason for stopping. As an abbreviation, I may give the name of a mathematical continuum of the first order to every aggregate of terms formed after the same law as the scale of commensurable numbers. If, then, we intercalate new sets according to the laws of incommensurable numbers, we obtain what may be called a continuum of the second order.

*Second Stage.*—We have only taken our first step. We have explained the origin of continuums of the first order; we must now see why this is not sufficient, and why the incommensurable numbers had to be invented.

If we try to imagine a line, it must have the characters of the physical continuum—that is to say, our representation must have a certain breadth. Two lines will therefore appear to us under the form of two narrow bands, and if we are content with this rough image, it is clear that where two lines cross they must have some common part. But the pure geometer makes one further effort; without entirely renouncing the aid of his senses, he tries to imagine a line without breadth and a point without size. This he can do only by imagining a line as the limit towards which tends a band that is growing thinner and thinner, and the point as the limit towards which is tending an area that is growing smaller and smaller. Our two bands, however narrow they may be, will always have a common area; the smaller they are the smaller it will be, and its limit is what the geometer calls a point. This is why it is said that the two lines which cross must have a common point, and this truth seems intuitive.

But a contradiction would be implied if we conceived of lines as continuums of the first order— *i.e.*, the lines traced by the geometer should only give us points, the co-ordinates of which are rational numbers. The contradiction would be manifest if we were, for instance, to assert the existence of lines and circles. It is clear, in fact, that if the points whose co-ordinates are commensurable were alone regarded as real, the in-circle of a square and the diagonal of the square would not intersect, since the co-ordinates of the point of intersection are incommensurable.

Even then we should have only certain incommensurable numbers, and not all these numbers.

But let us imagine a line divided into two half-rays (*demi-droites*). Each of these half-rays will appear to our minds as a band of a certain breadth; these bands will fit close together, because there must be no interval between them. The common part will appear to us to be a point which will still remain as we imagine the bands to become thinner and thinner, so that we admit as an intuitive truth that if a line be divided into two half-rays the common frontier of these half-rays is a point. Here we recognise the conception of Kronecker, in which an incommensurable number was regarded as the common frontier of two classes of rational numbers. Such is the origin of the continuum of the second order, which is the mathematical continuum properly so called.

*Summary.*—To sum up, the mind has the faculty of creating symbols, and it is thus that it has constructed the mathematical continuum, which is only a particular system of symbols. The only limit to its power is the necessity of avoiding all contradiction; but the mind only makes use of it when experiment gives a reason for it.

In the case with which we are concerned, the reason is given by the idea of the physical continuum, drawn from the rough data of the senses. But this idea leads to a series of contradictions from each of which in turn we must be freed. In this way we are forced to imagine a more and more complicated system of symbols. That on which we shall dwell is not merely exempt from internal contradiction,—it was so already at all the steps we have taken,—but it is no longer in contradiction with the various propositions which are called intuitive, and which are derived from more or less elaborate empirical notions.

*Measurable Magnitude.*—So far we have not spoken of the *measure* of magnitudes; we can tell if any one of them is greater than any other, but we cannot say that it is two or three times as large.

So far, I have only considered the order in which

the terms are arranged; but that is not sufficient for most applications. We must learn how to compare the interval which separates any two terms. On this condition alone will the continuum become measurable, and the operations of arithmetic be applicable. This can only be done by the aid of a new, and special convention; and this convention is, that in such a case the interval between the terms A and B is equal to the interval which separates C and D. For instance, we started with the integers, and between two consecutive sets we intercalated $n$ intermediary sets; by convention we now assume these new sets to be equidistant. This is one of the ways of defining the addition of two magnitudes; for if the interval AB is by definition equal to the interval CD, the interval AD will by definition be the sum of the intervals AB and AC. This definition is very largely, but not altogether, arbitrary. It must satisfy certain conditions—the commutative and associative laws of addition, for instance; but, provided the definition we choose satisfies these laws, the choice is indifferent, and we need not state it precisely.

*Remarks.*—We are now in a position to discuss several important questions.

(1) Is the creative power of the mind exhausted by the creation of the mathematical continuum? The answer is in the negative, and this is shown in a very striking manner by the work of Du Bois Reymond.

We know that mathematicians distinguish between infinitesimals of different orders, and that infinitesimals of the second order are infinitely small, not only absolutely so, but also in relation to those of the first order. It is not difficult to imagine infinitesimals of fractional or even of irrational order, and here once more we find the mathematical continuum which has been dealt with in the preceding pages. Further, there are infinitesimals which are infinitely small with reference to those of the first order, and infinitely large with respect to the order $1 + \epsilon$, however small $\epsilon$ may be. Here, then, are new terms intercalated in our series; and if I may be permitted to revert to the terminology used in the preceding pages, a terminology which is very convenient, although it has not been consecrated by usage, I shall say that we have created a kind of continuum of the third order.

It is an easy matter to go further, but it is idle to do so, for we would only be imagining symbols without any possible application, and no one will dream of doing that. This continuum of the third order, to which we are led by the consideration of the different orders of infinitesimals, is in itself of but little use and hardly worth quoting. Geometers look on it as a mere curiosity. The mind only uses its creative faculty when experiment requires it.

(2) When we are once in possession of the conception of the mathematical continuum, are

we protected from contradictions analogous to those which gave it birth? No, and the following is an instance:—

He is a *savant* indeed who will not take it as evident that every curve has a tangent; and, in fact, if we think of a curve and a straight line as two narrow bands, we can always arrange them in such a way that they have a common part without intersecting. Suppose now that the breadth of the bands diminishes indefinitely: the common part will still remain, and in the limit, so to speak, the two lines will have a common point, although they do not intersect—*i.e.*, they will touch. The geometer who reasons in this way is only doing what we have done when we proved that two lines which intersect have a common point, and his intuition might also seem to be quite legitimate. But this is not the case. We can show that there are curves which have no tangent, if we define such a curve as an analytical continuum of the second order. No doubt some artifice analogous to those we have discussed above would enable us to get rid of this contradiction, but as the latter is only met with in very exceptional cases, we need not trouble to do so. Instead of endeavouring to reconcile intuition and analysis, we are content to sacrifice one of them, and as analysis must be flawless, intuition must go to the wall.

*The Physical Continuum of several Dimensions.*— We have discussed above the physical continuum as it is derived from the immediate evidence of our

senses—or, if the reader prefers, from the rough
results of Fechner's experiments; I have shown
that these results are summed up in the contradictory formulæ:—A＝B, B＝C, A ＜ C.

Let us now see how this notion is generalised,
and how from it may be derived the concept of
continuums of several dimensions.   Consider any
two aggregates of sensations.   We can either
distinguish between them, or we cannot; just as in
Fechner's experiments the weight of 10 grammes
could be distinguished from the weight of 12
grammes, but not from the weight of 11 grammes.
This is all that is required to construct the continuum of several dimensions.

Let us call one of these aggregates of sensations
an *element*.   It will be in a measure analogous to
the *point* of the mathematicians, but will not be,
however, the same thing.   We cannot say that
our element has no size, for we cannot distinguish
it from its immediate neighbours, and it is thus
surrounded by a kind of fog.   If the astronomical
comparison may be allowed, our "elements"
would be like nebulæ, whereas the mathematical
points would be like stars.

If this be granted, a system of elements will
form a continuum, if we can pass from any one of
them to any other by a series of consecutive
elements such that each cannot be distinguished
from its predecessor.   This *linear* series is to the
*line* of the mathematician what the isolated *element*
was to the point.

Before going further, I must explain what is meant by a *cut*. Let us consider a continuum C, and remove from it certain of its elements, which for a moment we shall regard as no longer belonging to the continuum. We shall call the aggregate of elements thus removed a *cut*. By means of this cut, the continuum C will be *subdivided* into several distinct continuums; the aggregate of elements which remain will cease to form a single continuum. There will then be on C two elements, A and B, which we must look upon as belonging to two distinct continuums; and we see that this must be so, because it will be impossible to find a linear series of consecutive elements of C (each of the elements indistinguishable from the preceding, the first being A and the last B), *unless one of the elements of this series is indistinguishable from one of the elements of the cut.*

It may happen, on the contrary, that the cut may not be sufficient to subdivide the continuum C. To classify the physical continuums, we must first of all ascertain the nature of the cuts which must be made in order to subdivide them. If a physical continuum, C, may be subdivided by a cut reducing to a finite number of elements, all distinguishable the one from the other (and therefore forming neither one continuum nor several continuums), we shall call C a continuum *of one dimension*. If, on the contrary, C can only be subdivided by cuts which are themselves continuums, we shall say that C is of several dimensions; if the cuts are continuums of one dimension, then we shall say that C has two dimensions; if cuts of two dimensions are sufficient, we shall say that C is of three dimensions, and so on. Thus the notion of the physical continuum of several dimensions is defined, thanks to the very simple fact, that two aggregates of sensations may be distinguishable or indistinguishable.

*The Mathematical Continuum of Several Dimensions.* —The conception of the mathematical continuum of *n* dimensions may be led up to quite naturally by a process similar to that which we discussed at the beginning of this chapter. A point of such a continuum is defined by a system of *n* distinct magnitudes which we call its co-ordinates.

The magnitudes need not always be measurable; there is, for instance, one branch of geometry independent of the measure of magnitudes, in which we are only concerned with knowing, for example, if, on a curve A B C, the point B is between the points A and C, and in which it is immaterial whether the arc A B is equal to or twice the arc B C. This branch is called *Analysis Situs*. It contains quite a large body of doctrine which has attracted the attention of the greatest geometers, and from which are derived, one from another, a whole series of remarkable theorems. What distinguishes these theorems from those of ordinary geometry is that they are purely qualitative. They are still true if the figures are copied by an unskilful draughtsman, with the result that the proportions are distorted and the straight lines replaced by lines which are more or less curved.

As soon as measurement is introduced into the continuum we have just defined, the continuum becomes space, and geometry is born. But the discussion of this is reserved for Part II.

# PART II.

## *SPACE.*

## CHAPTER III.

### NON-EUCLIDEAN GEOMETRIES.

EVERY conclusion presumes premisses. These premisses are either self-evident and need no demonstration, or can be established only if based on other propositions; and, as we cannot go back in this way to infinity, every deductive science, and geometry in particular, must rest upon a certain number of indemonstrable axioms. All treatises of geometry begin therefore with the enunciation of these axioms. But there is a distinction to be drawn between them. Some of these, for example, "Things which are equal to the same thing are equal to one another," are not propositions in geometry but propositions in analysis. I look upon them as analytical *à priori* intuitions, and they concern me no further. But I must insist on other axioms which are special to geometry. Of these most treatises explicitly enunciate three :—(1) Only one line can pass through two points; (2) a straight line is the shortest distance between two points; (3) through one point only one parallel can be drawn to a given straight line.    Although we generally dispense with proving the second of these axioms, it would be possible to deduce it from the other two, and from those much more numerous axioms which are implicitly admitted without enunciation, as I shall explain further on.    For a long time a proof of the third axiom known as Euclid's postulate was sought in vain.    It is impossible to imagine the efforts that have been spent in pursuit of this chimera.    Finally, at the beginning of the nineteenth century, and almost simultaneously, two scientists, a Russian and a Bulgarian, Lobatschewsky and Bolyai, showed irrefutably that this proof is impossible.    They have nearly rid us of inventors of geometries without a postulate, and ever since the Académie des Sciences receives only about one or two new demonstrations a year. But the question was not exhausted, and it was not long before a great step was taken by the celebrated memoir of Riemann, entitled: *Ueber die Hypothesen welche der Geometrie zum Grunde liegen.*    This little work has inspired most of the recent treatises to which I shall later on refer, and among which I may mention those of Beltrami and Helmholtz.

*The Geometry of Lobatschewsky.* — If it were possible to deduce Euclid's postulate from the several axioms, it is evident that by rejecting the postulate and retaining the other axioms we should be led to contradictory consequences. It would be, therefore, impossible to found on those premises a coherent geometry. Now, this is precisely what Lobatschewsky has done. He assumes at the outset that several parallels may be drawn through a point to a given straight line, and he retains all the other axioms of Euclid. From these hypotheses he deduces a series of theorems between which it is impossible to find any contradiction, and he constructs a geometry as impeccable in its logic as Euclidean geometry. The theorems are very different, however, from those to which we are accustomed, and at first will be found a little disconcerting. For instance, the sum of the angles of a triangle is always less than two right angles, and the difference between that sum and two right angles is proportional to the area of the triangle. It is impossible to construct a figure similar to a given figure but of different dimensions. If the circumference of a circle be divided into $n$ equal parts, and tangents be drawn at the points of intersection, the $n$ tangents will form a polygon if the radius of the circle is small enough, but if the radius is large enough they will never meet. We need not multiply these examples. Lobatschewsky's propositions have no relation to those of Euclid, but they are none the less logically interconnected.

*Riemann's Geometry.*—Let us imagine to ourselves a world only peopled with beings of no thickness, and suppose these "infinitely flat" animals are all in one and the same plane, from which they cannot emerge.  Let us further admit that this world is sufficiently distant from other worlds to be withdrawn from their influence, and while we are making these hypotheses it will not cost us much to endow these beings with reasoning power, and to believe them capable of making a geometry.  In that case they will certainly attribute to space only two dimensions.  But now suppose that these imaginary animals, while remaining without thickness, have the form of a spherical, and not of a plane figure, and are all on the same sphere, from which they cannot escape. What kind of a geometry will they construct?  In the first place, it is clear that they will attribute to space only two dimensions.  The straight line to them will be the shortest distance from one point on the sphere to another—that is to say, an arc of a great circle.  In a word, their geometry will be spherical geometry.  What they will call space will be the sphere on which they are confined, and on which take place all the phenomena with which they are acquainted.  Their space will therefore be *unbounded*, since on a sphere one may always walk forward without ever being brought to a stop, and yet it will be *finite;* the end will never be found, but the complete tour can be made.  Well, Riemann's geometry is spherical geometry extended to three dimensions.  To construct it, the German mathematician had first of all to throw overboard, not only Euclid's postulate, but also the first axiom that *only one line can pass through two points.* On a sphere, through two given points, we can *in general* draw only one great circle which, as we have just seen, would be to our imaginary beings a straight line. But there was one exception. If the two given points are at the ends of a diameter, an infinite number of great circles can be drawn through them. In the same way, in Riemann's geometry—at least in one of its forms—through two points only one straight line can in general be drawn, but there are exceptional cases in which through two points an infinite number of straight lines can be drawn. So there is a kind of opposition between the geometries of Riemann and Lobatschewsky. For instance, the sum of the angles of a triangle is equal to two right angles in Euclid's geometry, less than two right angles in that of Lobat-schewsky, and greater than two right angles in that of Riemann. The number of parallel lines that can be drawn through a given point to a given line is one in Euclid's geometry, none in Riemann's, and an infinite number in the geometry of Lobat-schewsky. Let us add that Riemann's space is finite, although unbounded in the sense which we have above attached to these words.

*Surfaces with Constant Curvature.*—One objection, however, remains possible. There is no contradiction between the theorems of Lobatschewsky and Riemann; but however numerous are the other consequences that these geometers have deduced from their hypotheses, they had to arrest their course before they exhausted them all, for the number would be infinite; and who can say that if they had carried their deductions further they would not have eventually reached some contradiction? This difficulty does not exist for Riemann's geometry, provided it is limited to two dimensions. As we have seen, the two-dimensional geometry of Riemann, in fact, does not differ from spherical geometry, which is only a branch of ordinary geometry, and is therefore outside all contradiction. Beltrami, by showing that Lobatschewsky's two-dimensional geometry was only a branch of ordinary geometry, has equally refuted the objection as far as it is concerned. This is the course of his argument: Let us consider any figure whatever on a surface. Imagine this figure to be traced on a flexible and inextensible canvas applied to the surface, in such a way that when the canvas is displaced and deformed the different lines of the figure change their form without changing their length. As a rule, this flexible and inextensible figure cannot be displaced without leaving the surface. But there are certain surfaces for which such a movement would be possible. They are surfaces of constant curvature. If we resume the comparison that we made just now, and imagine beings without thickness living on one of these surfaces, they will regard as possible the motion of a figure all the lines of which remain of a constant length. Such a movement would appear absurd, on the other hand, to animals without thickness living on a surface of variable curvature. These surfaces of constant curvature are of two kinds. The curvature of some is *positive*, and they may be deformed so as to be applied to a sphere. The geometry of these surfaces is therefore reduced to spherical geometry—namely, Riemann's. The curvature of others is *negative*. Beltrami has shown that the geometry of these surfaces is identical with that of Lobatschewsky. Thus the two-dimensional geometries of Riemann and Lobatschewsky are connected with Euclidean geometry.

*Interpretation of Non-Euclidean Geometries.*—Thus vanishes the objection so far as two-dimensional geometries are concerned. It would be easy to extend Beltrami's reasoning to three-dimensional geometries, and minds which do not recoil before space of four dimensions will see no difficulty in it; but such minds are few in number. I prefer, then, to proceed otherwise. Let us consider a certain plane, which I shall call the fundamental plane, and let us construct a kind of dictionary by making a double series of terms written in two columns, and corresponding each to each, just as in ordinary dictionaries the words in two languages which have the same signification correspond to one another:—

Space ... ... ... The portion of space situated above the fundamental plane.

| | |
|---|---|
| Plane ... ... ... | Sphere cutting orthogonally the fundamental plane. |
| Line ... ... ... | Circle cutting orthogonally the fundamental plane. |
| Sphere ... ... ... | Sphere. |
| Circle ... ... ... | Circle. |
| Angle ... ... ... | Angle. |
| Distance between two points ... | Logarithm of the anharmonic ratio of these two points and of the intersection of the fundamental plane with the circle passing through these two points and cutting it orthogonally. |
| Etc. | Etc. |

Let us now take Lobatschewsky's theorems and translate them by the aid of this dictionary, as we would translate a German text with the aid of a German - French dictionary. *We shall then obtain the theorems of ordinary geometry.* For instance, Lobatschewsky's theorem: " The sum of the angles of a triangle is less than two right angles," may be translated thus: " If a curvilinear triangle has for its sides arcs of circles which if produced would cut orthogonally the fundamental plane, the sum of the angles of this curvilinear triangle will be less than two right angles." Thus, however far the consequences of Lobatschewsky's hypotheses are carried, they will never lead to a contradiction; in fact, if two of Lobatschewsky's theorems were contradictory, the translations of these two theorems made by the aid of our dictionary would be contradictory also. But these translations are theorems of ordinary geometry, and no one doubts that ordinary geometry is exempt from contradiction. Whence is the certainty derived, and how far is it justified? That is a question upon which I cannot enter here, but it is a very interesting question, and I think not insoluble. Nothing, therefore, is left of the objection I formulated above. But this is not all. Lobatschewsky's geometry being susceptible of a concrete interpretation, ceases to be a useless logical exercise, and may be applied. I have no time here to deal with these applications, nor with what Herr Klein and myself have done by using them in the integration of linear equations. Further, this interpretation is not unique, and several dictionaries may be constructed analogous to that above, which will enable us by a simple translation to convert Lobatschewsky's theorems into the theorems of ordinary geometry.

*Implicit Axioms.* — Are the axioms implicitly enunciated in our text-books the only foundation of geometry? We may be assured of the contrary when we see that, when they are abandoned one after another, there are still left standing some propositions which are common to the geometries of Euclid, Lobatschewsky, and Riemann. These propositions must be based on premisses that geometers admit without enunciation. It is interesting to try and extract them from the classical proofs.

John Stuart Mill asserted[1] that every definition contains an axiom, because by defining we implicitly affirm the existence of the object defined. That is going rather too far. It is but rarely in mathematics that a definition is given without following it up by the proof of the existence of the object defined, and when this is not done it is generally because the reader can easily supply it; and it must not be forgotten that the word "existence" has not the same meaning when it refers to a mathematical entity as when it refers to a material object.

A mathematical entity exists provided there is no contradiction implied in its definition, either in itself, or with the propositions previously admitted. But if the observation of John Stuart Mill cannot be applied to all definitions, it is none the less true for some of them. A plane is sometimes defined in the following manner:—The plane is a surface such that the line which joins any two points upon it lies wholly on that surface. Now, there is obviously a new axiom concealed in this definition. It is true we might change it, and that would be preferable, but then we should have to enunciate the axiom explicitly. Other definitions may give rise to no less important reflections, such as, for example, that of the equality of two figures. Two

[1] *Logic*, c. viii., cf. Definitions, § 5-6.—TR.

figures are equal when they can be superposed. To superpose them, one of them must be displaced until it coincides with the other. But how must it be displaced? If we asked that question, no doubt we should be told that it ought to be done without deforming it, and as an invariable solid is displaced. The vicious circle would then be evident. As a matter of fact, this definition defines nothing. It has no meaning to a being living in a world in which there are only fluids. If it seems clear to us, it is because we are accustomed to the properties of natural solids which do not much differ from those of the ideal solids, all of whose dimensions are invariable. However, imperfect as it may be, this definition implies an axiom. The possibility of the motion of an invariable figure is not a self-evident truth. At least it is only so in the application to Euclid's postulate, and not as an analytical *à priori* intuition would be. Moreover, when we study the definitions and the proofs of geometry, we see that we are compelled to admit without proof not only the possibility of this motion, but also some of its properties. This first arises in the definition of the straight line. Many defective definitions have been given, but the true one is that which is understood in all the proofs in which the straight line intervenes. "It may happen that the motion of an invariable figure may be such that all the points of a line belonging to the figure are motionless, while all the points situate outside that line are in motion. Such a line would be called a straight line." We have deliberately in this enunciation separated the definition from the axiom which it implies. Many proofs such as those of the cases of the equality of triangles, of the possibility of drawing a perpendicular from a point to a straight line, assume propositions the enunciations of which are dispensed with, for they necessarily imply that it is possible to move a figure in space in a certain way.

*The Fourth Geometry.*—Among these explicit axioms there is one which seems to me to deserve some attention, because when we abandon it we can construct a fourth geometry as coherent as those of Euclid, Lobatschewsky, and Riemann. To prove that we can always draw a perpendicular at a point A to a straight line A B, we consider a straight line A C movable about the point A, and initially identical with the fixed straight line A B. We then can make it turn about the point A until it lies in A B produced. Thus we assume two propositions—first, that such a rotation is possible, and then that it may continue until the two lines lie the one in the other produced. If the first point is conceded and the second rejected, we are led to a series of theorems even stranger than those of Lobatschewsky and Riemann, but equally free from contradiction. I shall give only one of these theorems, and I shall not choose the least remarkable of them. *A real straight line may be perpendicular to itself.*

*Lie's Theorem.*—The number of axioms implicitly

introduced into classical proofs is greater than necessary, and it would be interesting to reduce them to a minimum. It may be asked, in the first place, if this reduction is possible—if the number of necessary axioms and that of imaginable geometries is not infinite? A theorem due to Sophus Lie is of weighty importance in this discussion. It may be enunciated in the following manner:—Suppose the following premisses are admitted: (1) space has $n$ dimensions; (2) the movement of an invariable figure is possible; (3) $p$ conditions are necessary to determine the position of this figure in space.

*The number of geometries compatible with these premisses will be limited.* I may even add that if $n$ is given, a superior limit can be assigned to $p$. If, therefore, the possibility of the movement is granted, we can only invent a finite and even a rather restricted number of three-dimensional geometries.

*Riemann's Geometries.* — However, this result seems contradicted by Riemann, for that scientist constructs an infinite number of geometries, and that to which his name is usually attached is only a particular case of them. All depends, he says, on the manner in which the length of a curve is defined. Now, there is an infinite number of ways of defining this length, and each of them may be the starting-point of a new geometry. That is perfectly true, but most of these definitions are incompatible with the movement of a variable figure such as we assume to be possible in Lie's theorem.

These geometries of Riemann, so interesting on various grounds, can never be, therefore, purely analytical, and would not lend themselves to proofs analogous to those of Euclid.

*On the Nature of Axioms.*—Most mathematicians regard Lobatschewsky's geometry as a mere logical curiosity. Some of them have, however, gone further. If several geometries are possible, they say, is it certain that our geometry is the one that is true? Experiment no doubt teaches us that the sum of the angles of a triangle is equal to two right angles, but this is because the triangles we deal with are too small. According to Lobatschewsky, the difference is proportional to the area of the triangle, and will not this become sensible when we operate on much larger triangles, and when our measurements become more accurate? Euclid's geometry would thus be a provisory geometry. Now, to discuss this view we must first of all ask ourselves, what is the nature of geometrical axioms? Are they synthetic *à priori* intuitions, as Kant affirmed? They would then be imposed upon us with such a force that we could not conceive of the contrary proposition, nor could we build upon it a theoretical edifice. There would be no non-Euclidean geometry. To convince ourselves of this, let us take a true synthetic *à priori* intuition—the following, for instance, which played an important part in the first chapter:—If a theorem is true for the number 1, and if it has been proved that it is true of $n + 1$, provided it is true of $n$, it will be true for all positive integers. Let us next try to get rid of this, and while rejecting this proposition let us construct a false arithmetic analogous to non-Euclidean geometry. We shall not be able to do it. We shall be even tempted at the outset to look upon these intuitions as analytical. Besides, to take up again our fiction of animals without thickness, we can scarcely admit that these beings, if their minds are like ours, would adopt the Euclidean geometry, which would be contradicted by all their experience. Ought we, then, to conclude that the axioms of geometry are experimental truths? But we do not make experiments on ideal lines or ideal circles; we can only make them on material objects. On what, therefore, would experiments serving as a foundation for geometry be based? The answer is easy. We have seen above that we constantly reason as if the geometrical figures behaved like solids. What geometry would borrow from experiment would be therefore the properties of these bodies. The properties of light and its propagation in a straight line have also given rise to some of the propositions of geometry, and in particular to those of projective geometry, so that from that point of view one would be tempted to say that metrical geometry is the study of solids, and projective geometry that of light. But a difficulty remains, and is unsurmountable. If geometry were an experimental science, it would not be an exact science. It would be subjected to

continual revision. Nay, it would from that day
forth be proved to be erroneous, for we know that
no rigorously invariable solid exists. *The geometrical axioms are therefore neither synthetic à priori
intuitions nor experimental facts.* They are conventions. Our choice among all possible conventions
is *guided* by experimental facts; but it remains
*free*, and is only limited by the necessity of avoiding every contradiction, and thus it is that postulates may remain rigorously true even when the
experimental laws which have determined their
adoption are only approximate. In other words,
*the axioms of geometry* (I do not speak of those of
arithmetic) *are only definitions in disguise.* What,
then, are we to think of the question: Is
Euclidean geometry true? It has no meaning.
We might as well ask if the metric system is true,
and if the old weights and measures are false; if
Cartesian co-ordinates are true and polar co-
ordinates false. One geometry cannot be more
true than another; it can only be more convenient.
Now, Euclidean geometry is, and will remain, the
most convenient: 1st, because it is the simplest,
and it is not so only because of our mental habits
or because of the kind of direct intuition that we
have of Euclidean space; it is the simplest in
itself, just as a polynomial of the first degree is
simpler than a polynomial of the second degree;
2nd, because it sufficiently agrees with the properties of natural solids, those bodies which we
can compare and measure by means of our senses.

# CHAPTER IV.

## SPACE AND GEOMETRY.

LET us begin with a little paradox. Beings whose minds were made as ours, and with senses like ours, but without any preliminary education, might receive from a suitably-chosen external world impressions which would lead them to construct a geometry other than that of Euclid, and to localise the phenomena of this external world in a non-Euclidean space, or even in space of four dimensions. As for us, whose education has been made by our actual world, if we were suddenly transported into this new world, we should have no difficulty in referring phenomena to our Euclidean space. Perhaps somebody may appear on the scene some day who will devote his life to it, and be able to represent to himself the fourth dimension.

*Geometrical Space and Representative Space.*—It is often said that the images we form of external objects are localised in space, and even that they can only be formed on this condition. It is also said that this space, which thus serves as a kind of framework ready prepared for our sensations and representations, is identical with the space of the

geometers, having all the properties of that space.
To all clear-headed men who think in this way,
the preceding statement might well appear extraordinary; but it is as well to see if they are not
the victims of some illusion which closer analysis
may be able to dissipate. In the first place, what
are the properties of space properly so called?
I mean of that space which is the object of
geometry, and which I shall call geometrical
space. The following are some of the more
essential:—

1st, it is continuous; 2nd, it is infinite; 3rd, it
is of three dimensions; 4th, it is homogeneous—
that is to say, all its points are identical one
with another; 5th, it is isotropic. Compare this
now with the framework of our representations
and sensations, which I may call *representative
space.*

*Visual Space.*—First of all let us consider a
purely visual impression, due to an image formed
on the back of the retina. A cursory analysis shows
us this image as continuous, but as possessing only
two dimensions, which already distinguishes purely
visual from what may be called geometrical space.
On the other hand, the image is enclosed within
a limited framework; and there is a no less
important difference: *this pure visual space is not
homogeneous.* All the points on the retina, apart
from the images which may be formed, do not
play the same rôle. The yellow spot can in no
way be regarded as identical with a point on the

edge of the retina. Not only does the same object produce on it much brighter impressions, but in the whole of the *limited* framework the point which occupies the centre will not appear identical with a point near one of the edges. Closer analysis no doubt would show us that this continuity of visual space and its two dimensions are but an illusion. It would make visual space even more different than before from geometrical space, but we may treat this remark as incidental.

However, sight enables us to appreciate distance, and therefore to perceive a third dimension. But every one knows that this perception of the third dimension reduces to a sense of the effort of accommodation which must be made, and to a sense of the convergence of the two eyes, that must take place in order to perceive an object distinctly. These are muscular sensations quite different from the visual sensations which have given us the concept of the two first dimensions. The third dimension will therefore not appear to us as playing the same rôle as the two others. What may be called *complete visual space* is not therefore an isotropic space. It has, it is true, exactly three dimensions; which means that the elements of our visual sensations (those at least which concur in forming the concept of extension) will be completely defined if we know three of them; or, in mathematical language, they will be functions of three independent variables. But let us look at the matter a little closer. The third dimension is revealed to us in two different ways: by the effort of accommodation, and by the convergence of the eyes. No doubt these two indications are always in harmony; there is between them a constant relation; or, in mathematical language, the two variables which measure these two muscular sensations do not appear to us as independent. Or, again, to avoid an appeal to mathematical ideas which are already rather too refined, we may go back to the language of the preceding chapter and enunciate the same fact as follows:—If two sensations of convergence A and B are indistinguishable, the two sensations of accommodation A' and B' which accompany them respectively will also be indistinguishable. But that is, so to speak, an experimental fact. Nothing prevents us *à priori* from assuming the contrary, and if the contrary takes place, if these two muscular sensations both vary independently, we must take into account one more independent variable, and complete visual space will appear to us as a physical continuum of four dimensions. And so in this there is also a fact of *external* experiment. Nothing prevents us from assuming that a being with a mind like ours, with the same sense-organs as ourselves, may be placed in a world in which light would only reach him after being passed through refracting media of complicated form. The two indications which enable us to appreciate distances would cease to be connected by a constant relation. A being educating his senses in such a world would no doubt attribute four dimensions to complete visual space.

*Tactile and Motor Space.*—"Tactile space" is more complicated still than visual space, and differs even more widely from geometrical space. It is useless to repeat for the sense of touch my remarks on the sense of sight. But outside the data of sight and touch there are other sensations which contribute as much and more than they do to the genesis of the concept of space. They are those which everybody knows, which accompany all our movements, and which we usually call muscular sensations. The corresponding framework constitutes what may be called *motor space*. Each muscle gives rise to a special sensation which may be increased or diminished so that the aggregate of our muscular sensations will depend upon as many variables as we have muscles. From this point of view *motor space would have as many dimensions as we have muscles*. I know that it is said that if the muscular sensations contribute to form the concept of space, it is because we have the sense of the *direction* of each movement, and that this is an integral part of the sensation. If this were so, and if a muscular sense could not be aroused unless it were accompanied by this geometrical sense of direction, geometrical space would certainly be a form imposed upon our sensitiveness. But I do not see this at all when I analyse my sensations. What I do see is that the sensations which correspond to movements in the same direction are connected in my mind by a simple *association of ideas*. It is to this association that what we call the sense of direction is reduced. We cannot therefore discover this sense in a single sensation. This association is extremely complex, for the contraction of the same muscle may correspond, according to the position of the limbs, to very different movements of direction. Moreover, it is evidently acquired; it is like all associations of ideas, the result of a *habit*. This habit itself is the result of a very large number of *experiments*, and no doubt if the education of our senses had taken place in a different medium, where we would have been subjected to different impressions, then contrary habits would have been acquired, and our muscular sensations would have been associated according to other laws.

*Characteristics of Representative Space.*—Thus representative space in its triple form — visual, tactile, and motor—differs essentially from geometrical space. It is neither homogeneous nor isotropic; we cannot even say that it is of three dimensions. It is often said that we "project" into geometrical space the objects of our external perception; that we "localise" them. Now, has that any meaning, and if so what is that meaning? Does it mean that we *represent* to ourselves external objects in geometrical space? Our representations are only the reproduction of our sensations; they cannot therefore be arranged in the same framework—that is to say, in representative

space. It is also just as impossible for us to represent to ourselves external objects in geometrical
space, as it is impossible for a painter.to paint on
a flat surface objects with their three dimensions.
Representative space is only an image of geometrical space, an image deformed by a kind of
perspective, and we can only represent to ourselves objects by making them obey the laws of
this perspective. Thus we do not *represent* to ourselves external bodies in geometrical space, but we
*reason* about these bodies as if they were situated
in geometrical space. When it is said, on the
other hand, that we "localise" such an object in
such a point of space, what does it mean? *It
simply means that we represent to ourselves the movements that must take place to reach that object.* And
it does not mean that to represent to ourselves
these movements they must be projected into
space, and that the concept of space must therefore
pre-exist. When I say that we represent to ourselves these movements, I only mean that we
represent to ourselves the muscular sensations
which accompany them, and which have no
geometrical character, and which therefore in no
way imply the pre-existence of the concept of
space.

*Changes of State and Changes of Position.*—But,
it may be said, if the concept of geometrical space
is not imposed upon our minds, and if, on the
other hand, none of our sensations can furnish us
with that concept, how then did it ever come into

existence? This is what we have now to examine, and it will take some time; but I can sum up in a few words the attempt at explanation which I am going to develop. *None of our sensations, if isolated, could have brought us to the concept of space; we are brought to it solely by studying the laws by which those sensations succeed one another.* We see at first that our impressions are subject to change; but among the changes that we ascertain, we are very soon led to make a distinction. Sometimes we say that the objects, the causes of these impressions, have changed their state, sometimes that they have changed their position, that they have only been displaced. Whether an object changes its state or only its position, this is always translated for us in the same manner, *by a modification in an aggregate of impressions.* How then have we been enabled to distinguish them? If there were only change of position, we could restore the primitive aggregate of impressions by making movements which would confront us with the movable object in the same *relative* situation. We thus *correct* the modification which was produced, and we re-establish the initial state by an inverse modification. If, for example, it were a question of the sight, and if an object be displaced before our eyes, we can "follow it with the eye," and retain its image on the same point of the retina by appropriate movements of the eyeball. These movements we are conscious of because they are voluntary, and because they are accompanied by

muscular sensations. But that does not mean
that we represent them to ourselves in geometrical
space. So what characterises change of position,
what distinguishes it from change of state, is that
it can always be *corrected* by this means. It may
therefore happen that we pass from the aggregate
of impressions A to the aggregate B in two different ways. First, involuntarily and without ex-
periencing muscular sensations—which happens
when it is the object that is displaced; secondly,
voluntarily, and with muscular sensation—which
happens when the object is motionless, but when
we displace ourselves in such a way that the
object has relative motion with respect to us. If
this be so, the translation of the aggregate A to
the aggregate B is only a change of position. It
follows that sight and touch could not have given
us the idea of space without the help of the
"muscular sense." Not only could this concept
not be derived from a single sensation, or even from
*a series of sensations;* but a *motionless* being could
never have acquired it, because, not being able to
correct by his movements the effects of the change
of position of external objects, he would have had
no reason to distinguish them from changes of
state. Nor would he have been able to acquire
it if his movements had not been voluntary,
or if they were unaccompanied by any sensations
whatever.

*Conditions of Compensation.*—How is such a
compensation possible in such a way that two

changes, otherwise mutually independent, may be
reciprocally corrected ? A mind *already familiar
with geometry* would reason as follows :—If there
is to be compensation, the different parts of the
external object on the one hand, and the different
organs of our senses on the other, must be in the
same *relative* position after the double change.
And for that to be the case, the different parts of
the external body on the one hand, and the different organs of our senses on the other, must have
the same relative position to each other after the
double change; and so with the different parts of
our body with respect to each other. In other
words, the external object in the first change must
be displaced as an invariable solid would be displaced, and it must also be so with the whole of our
body in the second change, which is to correct the
first. Under these conditions compensation may
be produced. But we who as yet know nothing of
geometry, whose ideas of space are not yet formed,
we cannot reason in this way—we cannot predict
*à priori* if compensation is possible. But experiment shows us that it sometimes does take place,
and we start from this experimental fact in order
to distinguish changes of state from changes of
position.

*Solid Bodies and Geometry.*—Among surrounding
objects there are some which frequently experience
displacements that may be thus corrected by a
*correlative* movement of our own body—namely,
*solid bodies.* The other objects, whose form is vari-

able, only in exceptional circumstances undergo
similar displacement (change of position without
change of form). When the displacement of a
body takes place with deformation, we can no
longer by appropriate movements place the organs
of our body in the same *relative* situation with
respect to this body; we can no longer, therefore,
reconstruct the primitive aggregate of impressions.

It is only later, and after a series of new experiments, that we learn how to decompose a body of
variable form into smaller elements such that each
is displaced approximately according to the same
laws as solid bodies. We thus distinguish "deformations" from other changes of state. In these
deformations each element undergoes a simple
change of position which may be corrected; but the
modification of the aggregate is more profound,
and can no longer be corrected by a correlative
movement. Such a concept is very complex even
at this stage, and has been relatively slow in
its appearance. It would not have been conceived
at all had not the observation of solid bodies shown
us beforehand how to distinguish changes of
position.

*If, then, there were no solid bodies in nature there
would be no geometry.*

Another remark deserves a moment's attention.
Suppose a solid body to occupy successively the
positions $\alpha$ and $\beta$; in the first position it will give
us an aggregate of impressions A, and in the second
position the aggregate of impressions B. Now let

there be a second solid body, of qualities entirely different from the first—of different colour, for instance. Assume it to pass from the position α, where it gives us the aggregate of impressions A′ to the position β, where it gives the aggregate of impressions B′. In general, the aggregate A will have nothing in common with the aggregate A′, nor will the aggregate B have anything in common with the aggregate B′. The transition from the aggregate A to the aggregate B, and that of the aggregate A′ to the aggregate B′, are therefore two changes which *in themselves* have in general nothing in common. Yet we consider both these changes as displacements; and, further, we consider them the *same* displacement. How can this be? It is simply because they may be both corrected by the *same* correlative movement of our body. "Correlative movement," therefore, constitutes the *sole connection* between two phenomena which otherwise we should never have dreamed of connecting.

On the other hand, our body, thanks to the number of its articulations and muscles, may have a multitude of different movements, but all are not capable of "correcting" a modification of external objects; those alone are capable of it in which our whole body, or at least all those in which the organs of our senses enter into play are displaced *en bloc*—*i.e.*, without any variation of their relative positions, as in the case of a solid body.

To sum up:

1. In the first place, we distinguish two categories of phenomena:—The first involuntary, unaccompanied by muscular sensations, and attributed to external objects—they are external changes; the second, of opposite character and attributed to the movements of our own body, are internal changes.

2. We notice that certain changes of each in these categories may be corrected by a correlative change of the other category.

3. We distinguish among external changes those that have a correlative in the other category—which we call displacements; and in the same way we distinguish among the internal changes those which have a correlative in the first category.

Thus by means of this reciprocity is defined a particular class of phenomena called displacements. *The laws of these phenomena are the object of geometry.*

*Law of Homogeneity.*—The first of these laws is the law of homogeneity. Suppose that by an external change we pass from the aggregate of impressions A to the aggregate B, and that then this change $\alpha$ is corrected by a correlative voluntary movement $\beta$, so that we are brought back to the aggregate A. Suppose now that another external change $\alpha'$ brings us again from the aggregate A to the aggregate B. Experiment then shows us that this change $\alpha'$, like the change $\alpha$, may be corrected by a voluntary correlative movement $\beta'$, and that this movement $\beta'$ corresponds to the same muscular sensations as the movement $\beta$ which corrected $\alpha$.

This fact is usually enunciated as follows:—*Space is homogeneous and isotropic.* We may also say that a movement which is once produced may be repeated a second and a third time, and so on, without any variation of its properties. In the first chapter, in which we discussed the nature of mathematical reasoning, we saw the importance that should be attached to the possibility of repeating the same operation indefinitely. The virtue of mathematical reasoning is due to this repetition; by means of the law of homogeneity geometrical facts are apprehended. To be complete, to the law of homogeneity must be added a multitude of other laws, into the details of which I do not propose to enter, but which mathematicians sum up by saying that these displacements form a "group."

*The Non-Euclidean World.*—If geometrical space were a framework imposed on *each* of our representations considered individually, it would be impossible to represent to ourselves an image without this framework, and we should be quite unable to change our geometry. But this is not the case; geometry is only the summary of the laws by which these images succeed each other. There is nothing, therefore, to prevent us from imagining a series of representations, similar in every way to our ordinary representations, but succeeding one another according to laws which differ from those to which we are accustomed. We may thus conceive that beings whose education has taken place in a medium in which those laws would be so different, might have a very different geometry from ours.

Suppose, for example, a world enclosed in a large sphere and subject to the following laws:—The temperature is not uniform; it is greatest at the centre, and gradually decreases as we move towards the circumference of the sphere, where it is absolute zero. The law of this temperature is as follows:— If $R$ be the radius of the sphere, and $r$ the distance of the point considered from the centre, the absolute temperature will be proportional to $R^2 - r^2$. Further, I shall suppose that in this world all bodies have the same co-efficient of dilatation, so that the linear dilatation of any body is proportional to its absolute temperature. Finally, I shall assume that a body transported from one point to another of different temperature is instantaneously in thermal equilibrium with its new environment. There is nothing in these hypotheses either contradictory or unimaginable. A moving object will become smaller and smaller as it approaches the circumference of the sphere. Let us observe, in the first place, that although from the point of view of our ordinary geometry this world is finite, to its inhabitants it will appear infinite. As they approach the surface of the sphere they become colder, and at the same time smaller and smaller. The steps they take are therefore also smaller and smaller, so that they can never reach the boundary of the sphere.  If to us geometry is only the study of the laws according to which invariable solids move, to these imaginary beings it will be the study of the laws of motion of solids *deformed by the differences of temperature* alluded to.

No doubt, in our world, natural solids also experience variations of form and volume due to differences of temperature.  But in laying the foundations of geometry we neglect these variations; for besides being but small they are irregular, and consequently appear to us to be accidental. In our hypothetical world this will no longer be the case, the variations will obey very simple and regular laws.  On the other hand, the different solid parts of which the bodies of these inhabitants are composed will undergo the same variations of form and volume.

Let me make another hypothesis: suppose that light passes through media of different refractive indices, such that the index of refraction is inversely proportional to $R^2-r^2$.  Under these conditions it is clear that the rays of light will no longer be rectilinear but circular.  To justify what has been said, we have to prove that certain changes in the position of external objects may be corrected by correlative movements of the beings which inhabit this imaginary world; and in such a way as to restore the primitive aggregate of the impressions experienced by these sentient beings.  Suppose, for example, that an object is displaced and deformed, not like an invariable solid, but like a solid subjected to unequal dilatations in exact conformity with the law of temperature assumed above. To use an abbreviation, we shall call such a movement a non-Euclidean displacement.

If a sentient being be in the neighbourhood of such a displacement of the object, his impressions will be modified; but by moving in a suitable manner, he may reconstruct them. For this purpose, all that is required is that the aggregate of the sentient being and the object, considered as forming a single body, shall experience one of those special displacements which I have just called non-Euclidean. This is possible if we suppose that the limbs of these beings dilate according to the same laws as the other bodies of the world they inhabit.

Although from the point of view of our ordinary geometry there is a deformation of the bodies in this displacement, and although their different parts are no longer in the same relative position, nevertheless we shall see that the impressions of the sentient being remain the same as before; in fact, though the mutual distances of the different parts have varied, yet the parts which at first were in contact are still in contact. It follows that tactile impressions will be unchanged. On the other hand, from the hypothesis as to refraction and the curvature of the rays of light, visual impressions will also be unchanged. These imaginary beings will therefore be led to classify the phenomena they observe, and to distinguish among them the " changes of position," which may be corrected by a voluntary correlative movement, just as we do.

If they construct a geometry, it will not be like ours, which is the study of the movements of our invariable solids; it will be the study of the changes of position which they will have thus distinguished, and will be "non-Euclidean displacements," and *this will be non-Euclidean geometry*. So that beings like ourselves, educated in such a world, will not have the same geometry as ours.

*The World of Four Dimensions.*—Just as we have pictured to ourselves a non-Euclidean world, so we may picture a world of four dimensions.

The sense of light, even with one eye, together with the muscular sensations relative to the movements of the eyeball, will suffice to enable us to conceive of space of three dimensions. The images of external objects are painted on the retina, which is a plane of two dimensions; these are *perspectives*. But as eye and objects are movable, we see in succession different perspectives of the same body taken from different points of view. We find at the same time that the transition from one perspective to another is often accompanied by muscular sensations. If the transition from the perspective A to the perspective B, and that of the perspective A' to the perspective B' are accompanied by the same muscular sensations, we connect them as we do other operations of the same nature. Then when we study the laws according to which these operations are combined, we see that they form a group, which has the same structure as that of the movements of invariable solids. Now, we have seen that it is from the properties of this group that we derive the idea of geometrical space and that of three dimensions. We thus understand how these perspectives gave rise to the conception of three dimensions, although each perspective is of only two dimensions,—because *they succeed each other according to certain laws*. Well, in the same way that we draw the perspective of a three-dimensional figure on a plane, so we can draw that of a four-dimensional figure on a canvas of three (or two) dimensions. To a geometer this is but child's play. We can even draw several perspectives of the same figure from several different points of view. We can easily represent to ourselves these perspectives, since they are of only three dimensions. Imagine that the different perspectives of one and the same object to occur in succession, and that the transition from one to the other is accompanied by muscular sensations. It is understood that we shall consider two of these transitions as two operations of the same nature when they are associated with the same muscular sensations. There is nothing, then, to prevent us from imagining that these operations are combined according to any law we choose—for instance, by forming a group with the same structure as that of the movements of an invariable four-dimensional solid.

In this there is nothing that we cannot represent to ourselves, and, moreover, these sensations are those which a being would experience who has a retina of two dimensions, and who may be displaced in space of four dimensions. In this sense we may say that we can represent to ourselves the fourth dimension.

*Conclusions.*—It is seen that experiment plays a considerable rôle in the genesis of geometry; but it would be a mistake to conclude from that that geometry is, even in part, an experimental science. If it were experimental, it would only be approximative and provisory. And what a rough approximation it would be! Geometry would be only the study of the movements of solid bodies; but, in reality, it is not concerned with natural solids: its object is certain ideal solids, absolutely invariable, which are but a greatly simplified and very remote image of them. The concept of these ideal bodies is entirely mental, and experiment is but the opportunity which enables us to reach the idea. The object of geometry is the study of a particular "group"; but the general concept of group pre-exists in our minds, at least potentially. It is imposed on us not as a form of our sensitiveness, but as a form of our understanding; only, from among all possible groups, we must choose one that will be the *standard*, so to speak, to which we shall refer natural phenomena.

Experiment guides us in this choice, which it does not impose on us. It tells us not what is the truest, but what is the most convenient geometry. It will be noticed that my description of these fantastic worlds has required no language other than that of ordinary geometry. Then, were we transported to those worlds, there would be no need to change that language. Beings educated there would no doubt find it more convenient to create a geometry different from ours, and better adapted to their impressions; but as for us, in the presence of the same impressions, it is certain that we should not find it more convenient to make a change.

# CHAPTER V.

### EXPERIMENT AND GEOMETRY.

1. I have on several occasions in the preceding pages tried to show how the principles of geometry are not experimental facts, and that in particular Euclid's postulate cannot be proved by experiment. However convincing the reasons already given may appear to me, I feel I must dwell upon them, because there is a profoundly false conception deeply rooted in many minds.

2. Think of a material circle, measure its radius and circumference, and see if the ratio of the two lengths is equal to $\pi$. What have we done? We have made an experiment on the properties of the matter with which this *roundness* has been realised, and of which the measure we used is made.

3. *Geometry and Astronomy.*—The same question may also be asked in another way. If Lobatschewsky's geometry is true, the parallax of a very distant star will be finite. If Riemann's is true, it will be negative. These are the results which seem within the reach of experiment, and it is hoped that astronomical observations may enable us to decide between the two geometries. But

what we call a straight line in astronomy is simply the path of a ray of light.   If, therefore, we were to discover negative parallaxes, or to prove that all parallaxes are higher than a certain limit, we should have a choice between two conclusions: we could give up Euclidean geometry, or modify the laws of optics, and suppose that light is not rigorously propagated in a straight line.   It is needless to add that every one would look upon this solution as the more advantageous.   Euclidean geometry, therefore, has nothing to fear from fresh experiments.

4. Can we maintain that certain phenomena which are possible in Euclidean space would be impossible in non-Euclidean space, so that experiment in establishing these phenomena would directly contradict the non-Euclidean hypothesis? I think that such a question cannot be seriously asked.   To me it is exactly equivalent to the following, the absurdity of which is obvious:—There are lengths which can be expressed in metres and centimetres, but cannot be measured in toises, feet, and inches; so that experiment, by ascertaining the existence of these lengths, would directly contradict this hypothesis, that there are toises divided into six feet.   Let us look at the question a little more closely.   I assume that the straight line in Euclidean space possesses any two properties, which I shall call A and B; that in non-Euclidean space it still possesses the property A, but no longer possesses the property B; and, finally, I

assume that in both Euclidean and non-Euclidean space the straight line is the only line that possesses the property A. If this were so, experiment would be able to decide between the hypotheses of Euclid and Lobatschewsky. It would be found that some concrete object, upon which we can experiment—for example, a pencil of rays of light—possesses the property A. We should conclude that it is rectilinear, and we should then endeavour to find out if it does, or does not, possess the property B. But *it is not so*. There exists no property which can, like this property A, be an absolute criterion enabling us to recognise the straight line, and to distinguish it from every other line. Shall we say, for instance, " This property will be the following: the straight line is a line such that a figure of which this line is a part can move without the mutual distances of its points varying, and in such a way that all the points in this straight line remain fixed "? Now, this is a property which in either Euclidean or non-Euclidean space belongs to the straight line, and belongs to it alone. But how can we ascertain by experiment if it belongs to any particular concrete object? Distances must be measured, and how shall we know that any concrete magnitude which I have measured with my material instrument really represents the abstract distance? We have only removed the difficulty a little farther off. In reality, the property that I have just enunciated is not a property of the straight line alone; it is a property of the straight line and of distance. For it to serve as an absolute criterion, we must be able to show, not only that it does not also belong to any other line than the straight line and to distance, but also that it does not belong to any other line than the straight line, and to any other magnitude than distance. Now, that is not true, and if we are not convinced by these considerations, I challenge any one to give me a concrete experiment which can be interpreted in the Euclidean system, and which cannot be interpreted in the system of Lobatschewsky. As I am well aware that this challenge will never be accepted, I may conclude that no experiment will ever be in contradiction with Euclid's postulate; but, on the other hand, no experiment will ever be in contradiction with Lobatschewsky's postulate.

5. But it is not sufficient that the Euclidean (or non-Euclidean) geometry can ever be directly contradicted by experiment. Nor could it happen that it can only agree with experiment by a violation of the principle of sufficient reason, and of that of the relativity of space. Let me explain myself. Consider any material system whatever. We have to consider on the one hand the "state" of the various bodies of this system—for example, their temperature, their electric potential, etc.; and on the other hand their position in space. And among the data which enable us to define this position we distinguish the mutual distances of these bodies that define their relative positions,

and the conditions which define the absolute position of the system and its absolute orientation in
space. The law of the phenomena which will be
produced in this system will depend on the state
of these bodies, and on their mutual distances;
but because of the relativity and the inertia of
space, they will not depend on the absolute position and orientation of the system. In other
words, the state of the bodies and their mutual
distances at any moment will solely depend on
the state of the same bodies and on their mutual
distances at the initial moment, but will in no
way depend on the absolute initial position of
the system and of its absolute initial orientation.
This is what we shall call, for the sake of
abbreviation, *the law of relativity*.

So far I have spoken as a Euclidean geometer.
But I have said that an experiment, whatever it
may be, requires an interpretation on the Euclidean
hypothesis; it equally requires one on the non-
Euclidean hypothesis. Well, we have made a series
of experiments. We have interpreted them on the
Euclidean hypothesis, and we have recognised
that these experiments thus interpreted do not
violate this "law of relativity." We now interpret
them on the non-Euclidean hypothesis. This is
always possible, only the non-Euclidean distances
of our different bodies in this new interpretation
will not generally be the same as the Euclidean
distances in the primitive interpretation. Will
our experiment interpreted in this new manner

be still in agreement with our "law of relativity," and if this agreement had not taken place, would we not still have the right to say that experiment has proved the falsity of non-Euclidean geometry? It is easy to see that this is an idle fear. In fact, to apply the law of relativity in all its rigour, it must be applied to the entire universe; for if we were to consider only a part of the universe, and if the absolute position of this part were to vary, the distances of the other bodies of the universe would equally vary; their influence on the part of the universe considered might therefore increase or diminish, and this might modify the laws of the phenomena which take place in it. But if our system is the entire universe, experiment is powerless to give us any opinion on its position and its absolute orientation in space. All that our instruments, however perfect they may be, can let us know will be the state of the different parts of the universe, and their mutual distances. Hence, our law of relativity may be enunciated as follows:—The readings that we can make with our instruments at any given moment will depend only on the readings that we were able to make on the same instruments at the initial moment. Now such an enunciation is independent of all interpretation by experiments. If the law is true in the Euclidean interpretation, it will be also true in the non-Euclidean interpretation. Allow me to make a short digression on this point. I have spoken above of the data which define the position of the different bodies of the system. I might also have spoken of those which define their velocities. I should then have to distinguish the velocity with which the mutual distances of the different bodies are changing, and on the other hand the velocities of translation and rotation of the system; that is to say, the velocities with which its absolute position and orientation are changing. For the mind to be fully satisfied, the law of relativity would have to be enunciated as follows:—The state of bodies and their mutual distances at any given moment, as well as the velocities with which those distances are changing at that moment, will depend only on the state of those bodies, on their mutual distances at the initial moment, and on the velocities with which those distances were changing at the initial moment. But they will not depend on the absolute initial position of the system nor on its absolute orientation, nor on the velocities with which that absolute position and orientation were changing at the initial moment. Unfortunately, the law thus enunciated does not agree with experiments—at least, as they are ordinarily interpreted. Suppose a man were translated to a planet, the sky of which was constantly covered with a thick curtain of clouds, so that he could never see the other stars. On that planet he would live as if it were isolated in space. But he would notice that it revolves, either by measuring its ellipticity (which is ordinarily done by means of astronomical observations, but which could be done by purely geodesic means), or by repeating the experiment of Foucault's pendulum. The absolute rotation of this planet might be clearly shown in this way. Now, here is a fact which shocks the philosopher, but which the physicist is compelled to accept. We know that from this fact Newton concluded the existence of absolute space. I myself cannot accept this way of looking at it. I shall explain why in Part III., but for the moment it is not my intention to discuss this difficulty. I must therefore resign myself, in the enunciation of the law of relativity, to including velocities of every kind among the data which define the state of the bodies. However that may be, the difficulty is the same for both Euclid's geometry and for Lobatschewsky's. I need not therefore trouble about it further, and I have only mentioned it incidentally. To sum up, whichever way we look at it, it is impossible to discover in geometric empiricism a rational meaning.

6. Experiments only teach us the relations of bodies to one another. They do not and cannot give us the relations of bodies and space, nor the mutual relations of the different parts of space. "Yes!" you reply, "a single experiment is not enough, because it only gives us one equation with several unknowns; but when I have made enough experiments I shall have enough equations to calculate all my unknowns." If I know the height of the main-mast, that is not sufficient to enable

me to calculate the age of the captain. When
you have measured every fragment of wood in a
ship you will have many equations, but you will
be no nearer knowing the captain's age. All your
measurements bearing on your fragments of wood
can tell you only what concerns those fragments;
and similarly, your experiments, however numerous
they may be, referring only to the relations of
bodies with one another, will tell you nothing
about the mutual relations of the different parts
of space.

7. Will you say that if the experiments have
reference to the bodies, they at least have reference
to the geometrical properties of the bodies. First,
what do you understand by the geometrical properties of bodies? I assume that it is a question
of the relations of the bodies to space. These
properties therefore are not reached by experiments which only have reference to the relations
of bodies to one another, and that is enough to
show that it is not of those properties that there
can be a question. Let us therefore begin by
making ourselves clear as to the sense of the
phrase: geometrical properties of bodies. When
I say that a body is composed of several parts, I
presume that I am thus enunciating a geometrical
property, and that will be true even if I agree to
give the improper name of points to the very
small parts I am considering. When I say that
this or that part of a certain body is in contact
with this or that part of another body, I am

enunciating a proposition which concerns the mutual relations of the two bodies, and not their relations with space. I assume that you will agree with me that these are not geometrical properties. I am sure that at least you will grant that these properties are independent of all knowledge of metrical geometry. Admitting this, I suppose that we have a solid body formed of eight thin iron rods, *oa, ob, oc, od, oe, of, og, oh,* connected at one of their extremities, *o*. And let us take a second solid body—for example, a piece of wood, on which are marked three little spots of ink which I shall call *α β γ.* I now suppose that we find that we can bring into contact *α β γ* with *ago;* by that I mean *α* with *a*, and at the same time *β* with *g*, and *γ* with *o.* Then we can successively bring into contact *αβγ* with *bgo, cgo, dgo, ego, fgo,* then with *aho, bho, cho, dho, eho, fho;* and then *αγ* successively with *ab, bc, cd, de, ef, fa.* Now these are observations that can be made without having any idea beforehand as to the form or the metrical properties of space. They have no reference whatever to the "geometrical properties of bodies." These observations will not be possible if the bodies on which we experiment move in a group having the same structure as the Lobatschewskian group (I mean according to the same laws as solid bodies in Lobatschewsky's geometry). They therefore suffice to prove that these bodies move according to the Euclidean group; or at least that they do not move according to the Lobatschewskian group. That they may be compatible with the Euclidean group is easily seen; for we might make them so if the body $\alpha\beta\gamma$ were an invariable solid of our ordinary geometry in the shape of a right-angled triangle, and if the points *abcdefgh* were the vertices of a polyhedron formed of two regular hexagonal pyramids of our ordinary geometry having *abcdef* as their common base, and having the one *g* and the other *h* as their vertices. Suppose now, instead of the previous observations, we note that we can as before apply $\alpha\beta\gamma$ successively to *ago*, *bgo*, *cgo*, *dgo*, *ego*, *fgo*, *aho*, *bho*, *cho*, *dho*, *eho*, *fho*, and then that we can apply $\alpha\beta$ (and no longer $\alpha\gamma$) successively to *ab*, *bc*, *cd*, *de*, *ef*, and *fa*. These are observations that could be made if non-Euclidean geometry were true. If the bodies $\alpha\beta\gamma$, *oabcdefgh* were invariable solids, if the former were a right-angled triangle, and the latter a double regular hexagonal pyramid of suitable dimensions. These new verifications are therefore impossible if the bodies move according to the Euclidean group; but they become possible if we suppose the bodies to move according to the Lobatschewskian group. They would therefore suffice to show, if we carried them out, that the bodies in question do not move according to the Euclidean group. And so, without making any hypothesis on the form and the nature of space, on the relations of the bodies and space, and without attributing to bodies any geometrical property, I have made observations which have enabled me to show in one case that the bodies experimented upon move according to a group, the structure of which is Euclidean, and in the other case, that they move in a group, the structure of which is Lobatschewskian. It cannot be said that all the first observations would constitute an experiment proving that space is Euclidean, and the second an experiment proving that space is non-Euclidean; in fact, it might be imagined (note that I use the word *imagined*) that there are bodies moving in such a manner as to render possible the second series of observations: and the proof is that the first mechanic who came our way could construct it if he would only take the trouble. But you must not conclude, however, that space is non-Euclidean. In the same way, just as ordinary solid bodies would continue to exist when the mechanic had constructed the strange bodies I have just mentioned, he would have to conclude that space is both Euclidean and non-Euclidean. Suppose, for instance, that we have a large sphere of radius $R$, and that its temperature decreases from the centre to the surface of the sphere according to the law of which I spoke when I was describing the non-Euclidean world. We might have bodies whose dilatation is negligeable, and which would behave as ordinary invariable solids; and, on the other hand, we might have very dilatable bodies, which would behave as non-Euclidean solids. We might have two double pyramids *oabcdefgh* and

$o'a'b'c'd'e'f'g'h'$, and two triangles $\alpha\,\beta\,\gamma$ and $\alpha'\,\beta'\,\gamma'$. The first double pyramid would be rectilinear, and the second curvilinear. The triangle $\alpha\beta\gamma$ would consist of undilatable matter, and the other of very dilatable matter. We might therefore make our first observations with the double pyramid $o'a'h'$ and the triangle $\alpha'\,\beta'\,\gamma'$.

And then the experiment would seem to show— first, that Euclidean geometry is true, and then that it is false. Hence, *experiments have reference not to space but to bodies.*

### SUPPLEMENT.

8. To round the matter off, I ought to speak of a very delicate question, which will require considerable development; but I shall confine myself to summing up what I have written in the *Revue de Métaphysique et de Morale* and in the *Monist.* When we say that space has three dimensions, what do we mean? We have seen the importance of these "internal changes" which are revealed to us by our muscular sensations. They may serve to characterise the different attitudes of our body. Let us take arbitrarily as our origin one of these attitudes, A. When we pass from this initial attitude to another attitude B we experience a series of muscular sensations, and this series S of muscular sensations will define B. Observe, however, that we shall often look upon two series S and S′ as defining the same attitude B (since the

initial and final attitudes A and B remaining the
same, the intermediary attitudes of the corresponding sensations may differ). How then can
we recognise the equivalence of these two series?
Because they may serve to compensate for the same
external change, or more generally, because, when
it is a question of compensation for an external
change, one of the series may be replaced by the
other. Among these series we have distinguished
those which can alone compensate for an external
change, and which we have called "displacements."
As we cannot distinguish two displacements which
are very close together, the aggregate of these
displacements presents the characteristics of a
physical continuum. Experience teaches us that
they are the characteristics of a physical continuum of six dimensions; but we do not know as
yet how many dimensions space itself possesses, so
we must first of all answer another question.
What is a point in space? Every one thinks he
knows, but that is an illusion. What we see when
we try to represent to ourselves a point in space is
a black spot on white paper, a spot of chalk on
a blackboard, always an object. The question
should therefore be understood as follows:—What
do I mean when I say the object B is at the
point which a moment before was occupied by the
object A? Again, what criterion will enable
me to recognise it? I mean that *although I have
not moved* (my muscular sense tells me this), my
finger, which just now touched the object A, is

now touching the object B. I might have used other criteria—for instance, another finger or the sense of sight—but the first criterion is sufficient. I know that if it answers in the affirmative all other criteria will give the same answer. I know it from experiment. I cannot know it *à priori*. For the same reason I say that touch cannot be exercised at a distance; that is another way of enunciating the same experimental fact. If I say, on the contrary, that sight is exercised at a distance, it means that the criterion furnished by sight may give an affirmative answer while the others reply in the negative.

To sum up. For each attitude of my body my finger determines a point, and it is that and that only which defines a point in space. To each attitude corresponds in this way a point. But it often happens that the same point corresponds to several different attitudes (in this case we say that our finger has not moved, but the rest of our body has). We distinguish, therefore, among changes of attitude those in which the finger does not move. How are we led to this? It is because we often remark that in these changes the object which is in touch with the finger remains in contact with it. Let us arrange then in the same class all the attitudes which are deduced one from the other by one of the changes that we have thus distinguished. To all these attitudes of the same class will correspond the same point in space. Then to each class will correspond a point, and to each point a class. Yet it may be said that what we get from this experiment is not the point, but the class of changes, or, better still, the corresponding class of muscular sensations. Thus, when we say that space has three dimensions, we merely mean that the aggregate of these classes appears to us with the characteristics of a physical continuum of three dimensions. Then if, instead of defining the points in space with the aid of the first finger, I use, for example, another finger, would the results be the same? That is by no means *à priori* evident. But, as we have seen, experiment has shown us that all our criteria are in agreement, and this enables us to answer in the affirmative. If we recur to what we have called displacements, the aggregate of which forms, as we have seen, a group, we shall be brought to distinguish those in which a finger does not move; and by what has preceded, those are the displacements which characterise a point in space, and their aggregate will form a sub-group of our group. To each sub-group of this kind, then, will correspond a point in space. We might be tempted to conclude that experiment has taught us the number of dimensions of space; but in reality our experiments have referred not to space, but to our body and its relations with neighbouring objects. What is more, our experiments are exceeding crude. In our mind the latent idea of a certain number of groups pre-existed; these are the groups with which Lie's theory is con-

cerned. Which shall we choose to form a kind of
standard by which to compare natural phenomena? And when this group is chosen, which
of the sub-groups shall we take to characterise a
point in space? Experiment has guided us by
showing us what choice adapts itself best to the
properties of our body; but there its rôle ends.

# PART III.

*FORCE.*

## CHAPTER VI.

### THE CLASSICAL MECHANICS.

THE English teach mechanics as an experimental science; on the Continent it is taught always more or less as a deductive and *à priori* science. The English are right, no doubt. How is it that the other method has been persisted in for so long; how is it that Continental scientists who have tried to escape from the practice of their predecessors have in most cases been unsuccessful? On the other hand, if the principles of mechanics are only of experimental origin, are they not merely approximate and provisory? May we not be some day compelled by new experiments to modify or even to abandon them? These are the questions which naturally arise, and the difficulty of solution is largely due to the fact that treatises on mechanics do not clearly distinguish between what is experiment, what is mathematical reasoning, what is convention, and what is hypothesis. This is not all.

1. There is no absolute space, and we only conceive of relative motion; and yet in most cases mechanical facts are enunciated as if there is an absolute space to which they can be referred.

2. There is no absolute time. When we say that two periods are equal, the statement has no meaning, and can only acquire a meaning by a convention.

3. Not only have we no direct intuition of the equality of two periods, but we have not even direct intuition of the simultaneity of two events occurring in two different places. I have explained this in an article entitled "Mesure du Temps." [1]

4. Finally, is not our Euclidean geometry in itself only a kind of convention of language? Mechanical facts might be enunciated with reference to a non-Euclidean space which would be less convenient but quite as legitimate as our ordinary space; the enunciation would become more complicated, but it still would be possible.

Thus, absolute space, absolute time, and even geometry are not conditions which are imposed on mechanics. All these things no more existed before mechanics than the French language can be logically said to have existed before the truths which are expressed in French. We might endeavour to enunciate the fundamental law of mechanics in a language independent of all these

[1] *Revue de Métaphysique et de Morale*, t. vi., pp. 1-13, January, 1898.

conventions; and no doubt we should in this way get a clearer idea of those laws in themselves. This is what M. Andrade has tried to do, to some extent at any rate, in his *Leçons de Mécanique physique*. Of course the enunciation of these laws would become much more complicated, because all these conventions have been adopted for the very purpose of abbreviating and simplifying the enunciation. As far as we are concerned, I shall ignore all these difficulties; not because I disregard them, far from it; but because they have received sufficient attention in the first two parts of the book. Provisionally, then, we shall admit absolute time and Euclidean geometry.

*The Principle of Inertia.* — A body under the action of no force can only move uniformly in a straight line. Is this a truth imposed on the mind *à priori*? If this be so, how is it that the Greeks ignored it? How could they have believed that motion ceases with the cause of motion? or, again, that every body, if there is nothing to prevent it, will move in a circle, the noblest of all forms of motion?

If it be said that the velocity of a body cannot change, if there is no reason for it to change, may we not just as legitimately maintain that the position of a body cannot change, or that the curvature of its path cannot change, without the agency of an external cause? Is, then, the principle of inertia, which is not an *à priori* truth, an experimental fact? Have there ever been experiments on bodies acted on by no forces? and, if so, how did we know that no forces were acting? The usual instance is that of a ball rolling for a very long time on a marble table; but why do we say it is under the action of no force? Is it because it is too remote from all other bodies to experience any sensible action? It is not further from the earth than if it were thrown freely into the air; and we all know that in that case it would be subject to the attraction of the earth. Teachers of mechanics usually pass rapidly over the example of the ball, but they add that the principle of inertia is verified indirectly by its consequences. This is very badly expressed; they evidently mean that various consequences may be verified by a more general principle, of which the principle of inertia is only a particular case. I shall propose for this general principle the following enunciation:—The acceleration of a body depends only on its position and that of neighbouring bodies, and on their velocities. Mathematicians would say that the movements of all the material molecules of the universe depend on differential equations of the second order. To make it clear that this is really a generalisation of the law of inertia we may again have recourse to our imagination. The law of inertia, as I have said above, is not imposed on us *à priori;* other laws would be just as compatible with the principle of sufficient reason. If a body is not acted upon by a force, instead of supposing that its velocity is unchanged we may suppose that its position or its acceleration is unchanged.

Let us for a moment suppose that one of these two laws is a law of nature, and substitute it for the law of inertia: what will be the natural generalisation? A moment's reflection will show us. In the first case, we may suppose that the velocity of a body depends only on its position and that of neighbouring bodies; in the second case, that the variation of the acceleration of a body depends only on the position of the body and of neighbouring bodies, on their velocities and accelerations; or, in mathematical terms, the differential equations of the motion would be of the first order in the first case and of the third order in the second.

Let us now modify our supposition a little. Suppose a world analogous to our solar system, but one in which by a singular chance the orbits of all the planets have neither eccentricity nor inclination; and further, I suppose that the masses of the planets are too small for their mutual perturbations to be sensible. Astronomers living in one of these planets would not hesitate to conclude that the orbit of a star can only be circular and parallel to a certain plane; the position of a star at a given moment would then be sufficient to determine its velocity and path. The law of inertia which they would adopt would be the former of the two hypothetical laws I have mentioned.

Now, imagine this system to be some day crossed by a body of vast mass and immense velocity coming from distant constellations. All the orbits would be profoundly disturbed. Our astronomers would not be greatly astonished. They would guess that this new star is in itself quite capable of doing all the mischief; but, they would say, as soon as it has passed by, order will again be established. No doubt the distances of the planets from the sun will not be the same as before the cataclysm, but the orbits will become circular again as soon as the disturbing cause has disappeared. It would be only when the perturbing body is remote, and when the orbits, instead of being circular are found to be elliptical, that the astronomers would find out their mistake, and discover the necessity of reconstructing their mechanics.

I have dwelt on these hypotheses, for it seems to me that we can clearly understand our generalised law of inertia only by opposing it to a contrary hypothesis.

Has this generalised law of inertia been verified by experiment, and can it be so verified? When Newton wrote the *Principia*, he certainly regarded this truth as experimentally acquired and demonstrated. It was so in his eyes, not only from the anthropomorphic conception to which I shall later refer, but also because of the work of Galileo. It was so proved by the laws of Kepler. According to those laws, in fact, the path of a planet is entirely determined by its initial position and initial velocity; this, indeed, is what our generalised law of inertia requires.

For this principle to be only true in appearance —lest we should fear that some day it must be replaced by one of the analogous principles which I opposed to it just now—we must have been led astray by some amazing chance such as that which had led into error our imaginary astronomers. Such an hypothesis is so unlikely that it need not delay us. No one will believe that there can be such chances; no doubt the probability that two eccentricities are both exactly zero is not smaller than the probability that one is 0.1 and the other 0.2. The probability of a simple event is not smaller than that of a complex one. If, however, the former does occur, we shall not attribute its occurrence to chance; we shall not be inclined to believe that nature has done it deliberately to deceive us. The hypothesis of an error of this kind being discarded, we may admit that so far as astronomy is concerned our law has been verified by experiment.

But Astronomy is not the whole of Physics. May we not fear that some day a new experiment will falsify the law in some domain of physics? An experimental law is always subject to revision; we may always expect to see it replaced by some other and more exact law. But no one seriously thinks that the law of which we speak will ever be abandoned or amended. Why?

Precisely because it will never be submitted to a decisive test.

In the first place, for this test to be complete, all the bodies of the universe must return with their initial velocities to their initial positions after a certain time. We ought then to find that they would resume their original paths. But this test is impossible; it can be only partially applied, and even when it is applied there will still be some bodies which will not return to their original positions. Thus there will be a ready explanation of any breaking down of the law.

Yet this is not all. In Astronomy we *see* the bodies whose motion we are studying, and in most cases we grant that they are not subject to the action of other invisible bodies. Under these conditions, our law must certainly be either verified or not. But it is not so in Physics. If physical phenomena are due to motion, it is to the motion of molecules which we cannot see. If, then, the acceleration of bodies we cannot see depends on something else than the positions or velocities of other visible bodies or of invisible molecules, the existence of which we have been led previously to admit, there is nothing to prevent us from supposing that this something else is the position or velocity of other molecules of which we have not so far suspected the existence. The law will be safeguarded. Let me express the same thought in another form in mathematical language. Suppose we are observing $n$ molecules, and find that their $3n$ co-ordinates satisfy a system of $3n$ differential equations of the fourth order (and not of the second, as required by the law of inertia). We know that by introducing $3n$ variable auxiliaries, a system of $3n$ equations of the fourth order may be reduced to a system of $6n$ equations of the second order. If, then, we suppose that the $3n$ auxiliary variables represent the co-ordinates of $n$ invisible molecules, the result is again conformable to the law of inertia. To sum up, this law, verified experimentally in some particular cases, may be extended fearlessly to the most general cases; for we know that in these general cases it can neither be confirmed nor contradicted by experiment.

*The Law of Acceleration.*—The acceleration of a body is equal to the force which acts on it divided by its mass.

Can this law be verified by experiment? If so, we have to measure the three magnitudes mentioned in the enunciation: acceleration, force, and mass. I admit that acceleration may be measured, because I pass over the difficulty arising from the measurement of time. But how are we to measure force and mass? We do not even know what they are. What is mass? Newton replies: "The product of the volume and the density." "It were better to say," answer Thomson and Tait, "that density is the quotient of the mass by the volume." What is force? "It is," replies Lagrange, "that which moves or tends to move a body." "It is," according to Kirchoff, "the product of the mass and the acceleiation." Then why not say that mass is the quotient of the force by the acceleration? These difficulties are insurmountable.

When we say force is the cause of motion, we are talking metaphysics; and this definition, if we had to be content with it, would be absolutely fruitless, would lead to absolutely nothing. For a definition to be of any use it must tell us how to measure force; and that is quite sufficient, for it is by no means necessary to tell what force is in itself, nor whether it is the cause or the effect of motion. We must therefore first define what is meant by the equality of two forces. When are two forces equal? We are told that it is when they give the same acceleration to the same mass, or when acting in opposite directions they are in equilibrium. This definition is a sham. A force applied to a body cannot be uncoupled and applied to another body as an engine is uncoupled from one train and coupled to another. It is therefore impossible to say what acceleration such a force, applied to such a body, would give to another body if it were applied to it. It is impossible to tell how two forces which are not acting in exactly opposite directions would behave if they were acting in opposite directions. It is this definition which we try to materialise, as it were, when we measure a force with a dynamometer or with a balance. Two forces, F and

F', which I suppose, for simplicity, to be acting vertically upwards, are respectively applied to two bodies, C and C'. I attach a body weighing P first to C and then to C'; if there is equilibrium in both cases I conclude that the two forces F and F' are equal, for they are both equal to the weight of the body P. But am I certain that the body P has kept its weight when I transferred it from the first body to the second? Far from it. I am certain of the contrary. I know that the magnitude of the weight varies from one point to another, and that it is greater, for instance, at the pole than at the equator. No doubt the difference is very small, and we neglect it in practice; but a definition must have mathematical rigour; this rigour does not exist. What I say of weight would apply equally to the force of the spring of a dynamometer, which would vary according to temperature and many other circumstances. Nor is this all. We cannot say that the weight of the body P is applied to the body C and keeps in equilibrium the force F. What is applied to the body C is the action of the body P on the body C. On the other hand, the body P is acted on by its weight, and by the reaction R of the body C on P the forces F and A are equal, because they are in equilibrium; the forces A and R are equal by virtue of the principle of action and reaction; and finally, the force R and the weight P are equal because they are in equilibrium. From these three equalities we deduce the equality of the weight P and the force F.

Thus we are compelled to bring into our definition of the equality of two forces the principle of the equality of action and reaction; *hence this principle can no longer be regarded as an experimental law but only as a definition.*

To recognise the equality of two forces we are then in possession of two rules: the equality of two forces in equilibrium and the equality of action and reaction. But, as we have seen, these are not sufficient, and we are compelled to have recourse to a third rule, and to admit that certain forces— the weight of a body, for instance—are constant in magnitude and direction. But this third rule is an experimental law. It is only approximately true: *it is a bad definition.* We are therefore reduced to Kirchoff's definition: force is the product of the mass and the acceleration. This law of Newton in its turn ceases to be regarded as an experimental law, it is now only a definition. But as a definition it is insufficient, for we do not know what mass is. It enables us, no doubt, to calculate the ratio of two forces applied at different times to the same body, but it tells us nothing about the ratio of two forces applied to two different bodies. To fill up the gap we must have recourse to Newton's third law, the equality of action and reaction, still regarded not as an experimental law but as a definition. Two bodies, A and B, act on each other; the acceleration of A, multiplied by the mass of A, is equal to the action of B on A; in the same way the acceleration of B, multiplied by the mass of B, is equal to the reaction of A on B. As, by definition, the action and the reaction are equal, the masses of A and B are respectively in the inverse ratio of their masses. Thus is the ratio of the two masses defined, and it is for experiment to verify that the ratio is constant.

This would do very well if the two bodies were alone and could be abstracted from the action of the rest of the world; but this is by no means the case. The acceleration of A is not solely due to the action of B, but to that of a multitude of other bodies, C, D, . . . To apply the preceding rule we must decompose the acceleration of A into many components, and find out which of these components is due to the action of B. The decomposition would still be possible if we suppose that the action of C on A is simply added to that of B on A, and that the presence of the body C does not in any way modify the action of B on A, or that the presence of B does not modify the action of C on A; that is, if we admit that any two bodies attract each other, that their mutual action is along their join, and is only dependent on their distance apart; if, in a word, we admit the *hypothesis of central forces.*

We know that to determine the masses of the heavenly bodies we adopt quite a different principle. The law of gravitation teaches us that the attraction of two bodies is proportional to their masses; if $r$ is their distance apart, $m$ and $m'$ their masses, $k$ a constant, then their attraction will be $kmm'/r^2$. What we are measuring is therefore not mass, the ratio of the force to the acceleration, but the attracting mass; not the inertia of the body, but its attracting power. It is an indirect process, the use of which is not indispensable theoretically. We might have said that the attraction is inversely proportional to the square of the distance, without being proportional to the product of the masses, that it is equal to $f/r^2$ and not to $kmm'$. If it were so, we should nevertheless, by observing the *relative* motion of the celestial bodies, be able to calculate the masses of these bodies.

But have we any right to admit the hypothesis of central forces? Is this hypothesis rigorously accurate? Is it certain that it will never be falsified by experiment? Who will venture to make such an assertion? And if we must abandon this hypothesis, the building which has been so laboriously erected must fall to the ground.

We have no longer any right to speak of the component of the acceleration of A which is due to the action of B. We have no means of distinguishing it from that which is due to the action of C or of any other body. The rule becomes inapplicable in the measurement of masses. What then is left of the principle of the equality of action and reaction? If we reject the hypothesis of central forces this principle must go too; the geometrical resultant of all the forces applied to the different bodies of a system abstracted from all external action will be zero. In other words, *the motion of the centre of gravity of this system will be uniform and in a straight line.* Here would seem to be a means of defining mass. The position of the centre of gravity evidently depends on the values given to the masses; we must select these values so that the motion of the centre of gravity is uniform and rectilinear. This will always be possible if Newton's third law holds good, and it will be in general possible only in one way. But no system exists which is abstracted from all external action; every part of the universe is subject, more or less, to the action of the other parts. *The law of the motion of the centre of gravity is only rigorously true when applied to the whole universe.*

But then, to obtain the values of the masses we must find the motion of the centre of gravity of the universe. The absurdity of this conclusion is obvious; the motion of the centre of gravity of the universe will be for ever to us unknown. Nothing, therefore, is left, and our efforts are fruitless. There is no escape from the following definition, which is only a confession of failure: *Masses are co-efficients which it is found convenient to introduce into calculations.*

We could reconstruct our mechanics by giving to our masses different values. The new mechanics would be in contradiction neither with experiment nor with the general principles of dynamics (the principle of inertia, proportionality of masses and accelerations, equality of action and reaction, uniform motion of the centre of gravity in a straight line, and areas). But the equations of this mechanics *would not be so simple.* Let us clearly understand this. It would be only the first terms which would be less simple—*i.e.,* those we already know through experiment; perhaps the small masses could be slightly altered without the *complete* equations gaining or losing in simplicity.

Hertz has inquired if the principles of mechanics are rigorously true. "In the opinion of many physicists it seems inconceivable that experiment will ever alter the impregnable principles of mechanics; and yet, what is due to experiment may always be rectified by experiment." From what we have just seen these fears would appear to be groundless. The principles of dynamics appeared to us first as experimental truths, but we have been compelled to use them as definitions. It is *by definition* that force is equal to the product of the mass and the acceleration; this is a principle which is henceforth beyond the reach of any future experiment. Thus it is by definition that action and reaction are equal and opposite. But then it will be said, these unverifiable principles are absolutely devoid of any significance. They cannot be disproved by experiment, but we can learn from them nothing of any use to us; what then is the use of studying dynamics? This somewhat rapid condemnation would be rather unfair. There is not in Nature any system *perfectly* isolated, perfectly abstracted from all external action; but there are systems which are *nearly* isolated. If we observe such a system, we can study not only the relative motion of its different parts with respect to each other, but the motion of its centre of gravity with respect to the other parts of the universe. We then find that the motion of its centre of gravity is *nearly* uniform and rectilinear in conformity with Newton's Third Law. This is an experimental fact, which cannot be invalidated by a more accurate experiment. What, in fact, would a more accurate experiment teach us? It would teach us that the law is only approximately true, and we know that already. *Thus is explained how experiment may serve as a basis for the principles of mechanics, and yet will never invalidate them.*

*Anthropomorphic Mechanics.*—It will be said that Kirchoff has only followed the general tendency of mathematicians towards nominalism; from this his skill as a physicist has not saved him. He wanted a definition of a force, and he took the first that came handy; but we do not require a definition of force; the idea of force is primitive, irreducible, indefinable; we all know what it is; of it we have direct intuition. This direct intuition arises from the idea of effort which is familiar to us from childhood. But in the first place, even if this direct intuition made known to us the real nature of force in itself, it would prove to be an insufficient basis for mechanics; it would, moreover, be quite useless. The important thing is not to know what force is, but how to measure it. Everything which does not teach us how to measure it is as useless to the mechanician as, for instance, the subjective idea of heat and cold to the student of heat. This subjective idea cannot be translated into numbers, and is therefore useless; a scientist whose skin is an absolutely bad conductor of heat, and who, therefore, has never felt the sensation of heat or cold, would read a thermometer in just the same way as any one else, and would have enough material to construct the whole of the theory of heat.

Now this immediate notion of effort is of no use to us in the measurement of force. It is clear, for example, that I shall experience more fatigue in lifting a weight of 100 lb. than a man who is accustomed to lifting heavy burdens. But there is more than this. This notion of effort does not teach us the nature of force; it is definitively reduced to a recollection of muscular sensations, and no one will maintain that the sun experiences a muscular sensation when it attracts the earth. All that we can expect to find from it is a symbol, less precise and less convenient than the arrows (to denote direction) used by geometers, and quite as remote from reality.

Anthropomorphism plays a considerable historic

rôle in the genesis of mechanics; perhaps it may yet furnish us with a symbol which some minds may find convenient; but it can be the foundation of nothing of a really scientific or philosophical character.

*The Thread School.*—M. Andrade, in his *Leçons de Mécanique physique*, has modernised anthropomorphic mechanics. To the school of mechanics with which Kirchoff is identified, he opposes a school which is quaintly called the "Thread School."

This school tries to reduce everything to the consideration of certain material systems of negligible mass, regarded in a state of tension and capable of transmitting considerable effort to distant bodies—systems of which the ideal type is the fine string, wire, or *thread*. A thread which transmits any force is slightly lengthened in the direction of that force; the direction of the thread tells us the direction of the force, and the magnitude of the force is measured by the lengthening of the thread.

We may imagine such an experiment as the following:—A body $A$ is attached to a thread; at the other extremity of the thread acts a force which is made to vary until the length of the thread is increased by $a$, and the acceleration of the body A is recorded. $A$ is then detached, and a body $B$ is attached to the same thread, and the same or another force is made to act until the increment of length again is $a$, and the acceleration of $B$ is noted. The experiment is then renewed with both $A$ and $B$ until the increment of length is $\beta$. The four accelerations observed should be proportional. Here we have an experimental verification of the law of acceleration enunciated above. Again, we may consider a body under the action of several threads in equal tension, and by experiment we determine the direction of those threads when the body is in equilibrium. This is an experimental verification of the law of the composition of forces. But, as a matter of fact, what have we done? We have defined the force acting on the string by the deformation of the thread, which is reasonable enough; we have then assumed that if a body is attached to this thread, the effort which is transmitted to it by the thread is equal to the action exercised by the body on the thread; in fact, we have used the principle of action and reaction by considering it, not as an experimental truth, but as the very definition of force. This definition is quite as conventional as that of Kirchoff, but it is much less general.

All the forces are not transmitted by the thread (and to compare them they would all have to be transmitted by identical threads). If we even admitted that the earth is attached to the sun by an invisible thread, at any rate it will be agreed that we have no means of measuring the increment of the thread. Nine times out of ten, in consequence, our definition will be in default; no sense of any kind can be attached to it, and we must fall back on that of Kirchoff. Why then go on in this roundabout way? You admit a certain definition of force which has a meaning only in certain particular cases. In those cases you verify by experiment that it leads to the law of acceleration. On the strength of these experiments you then take the law of acceleration as a definition of force in all the other cases.

Would it not be simpler to consider the law of acceleration as a definition in all cases, and to regard the experiments in question, not as verifications of that law, but as verifications of the principle of action and reaction, or as proving the deformations of an elastic body depend only on the forces acting on that body? Without taking into account the fact that the conditions in which your definition could be accepted can only be very imperfectly fulfilled, that a thread is never without mass, that it is never isolated from all other forces than the reaction of the bodies attached to its extremities.

The ideas expounded by M. Andrade are none the less very interesting. If they do not satisfy our logical requirements, they give us a better view of the historical genesis of the fundamental ideas of mechanics. The reflections they suggest show us how the human mind passed from a naïve anthropomorphism to the present conception of science.

We see that we end with an experiment which

is very particular, and as a matter of fact very crude, and we start with a perfectly general law, perfectly precise, the truth of which we regard as absolute. We have, so to speak, freely conferred this certainty on it by looking upon it as a convention.

Are the laws of acceleration and of the composition of forces only arbitrary conventions? Conventions, yes; arbitrary, no—they would be so if we lost sight of the experiments which led the founders of the science to adopt them, and which, imperfect as they were, were sufficient to justify their adoption. It is well from time to time to let our attention dwell on the experimental origin of these conventions.

# CHAPTER VII.

## RELATIVE AND ABSOLUTE MOTION.

*The Principle of Relative Motion.*—Sometimes endeavours have been made to connect the law of acceleration with a more general principle. The movement of any system whatever ought to obey the same laws, whether it is referred to fixed axes or to the movable axes which are implied in uniform motion in a straight line. This is the principle of relative motion; it is imposed upon us for two reasons: the commonest experiment confirms it; the consideration of the contrary hypothesis is singularly repugnant to the mind.

Let us admit it then, and consider a body under the action of a force. The relative motion of this body with respect to an observer moving with a uniform velocity equal to the initial velocity of the body, should be identical with what would be its absolute motion if it started from rest. We conclude that its acceleration must not depend upon its absolute velocity, and from that we attempt to deduce the complete law of acceleration.

For a long time there have been traces of this proof in the regulations for the degree of B. ès Sc.

It is clear that the attempt has failed. The obstacle which prevented us from proving the law of acceleration is that we have no definition of force. This obstacle subsists in its entirety, since the principle invoked has not furnished us with the missing definition. The principle of relative motion is none the less very interesting, and deserves to be considered for its own sake. Let us try to enunciate it in an accurate manner. We have said above that the accelerations of the different bodies which form part of an isolated system only depend on their velocities and their relative positions, and not on their velocities and their absolute positions, provided that the movable axes to which the relative motion is referred move uniformly in a straight line; or, if it is preferred, their accelerations depend only on the differences of their velocities and the differences of their co-ordinates, and not on the absolute values of these velocities and co-ordinates. If this principle is true for relative accelerations, or rather for differences of acceleration, by combining it with the law of reaction we shall deduce that it is true for absolute accelerations. It remains to be seen how we can prove that differences of acceleration depend only on differences of velocities and co-ordinates; or, to speak in mathematical language, that these differences of co-ordinates satisfy differential equations of the second order. Can this proof be deduced from experiment or from *à priori* conditions? Remembering what we

have said before, the reader will give his own
answer.  Thus enunciated, in fact, the principle of
relative motion curiously resembles what I called
above the generalised principle of inertia; it is not
quite the same thing, since it is a question of
differences of co-ordinates, and not of the co-
ordinates themselves.  The new principle teaches
us something more than the old, but the same
discussion applies to it, and would lead to the
same conclusions.  We need not recur to it.

*Newton's Argument.*—Here we find a very important and even slightly disturbing question.  I
have said that the principle of relative motion
was not for us simply a result of experiment; and
that *à priori* every contrary hypothesis would be
repugnant to the mind.  But, then, why is the
principle only true if the motion of the movable
axes is uniform and in a straight line?  It seems
that it should be imposed upon us with the same
force if the motion is accelerated, or at any rate
if it reduces to a uniform rotation.  In these two
cases, in fact, the principle is not true.  I need not
dwell on the case in which the motion of the
axes is in a straight line and not uniform.  The
paradox does not bear a moment's examination.
If I am in a railway carriage, and if the train,
striking against any obstacle whatever, is suddenly
stopped, I shall be projected on to the opposite
side, although I have not been directly acted upon
by any force.  There is nothing mysterious in
that, and if I have not been subject to the action

of any external force, the train has experienced an external impact. There can be nothing paradoxical in the relative motion of two bodies being disturbed when the motion of one or the other is modified by an external cause. Nor need I dwell on the case of relative motion referring to axes which rotate uniformly. If the sky were for ever covered with clouds, and if we had no means of observing the stars, we might, nevertheless, conclude that the earth turns round. We should be warned of this fact by the flattening at the poles, or by the experiment of Foucault's pendulum. And yet, would there in this case be any meaning in saying that the earth turns round? If there is no absolute space, can a thing turn without turning with respect to something; and, on the other hand, how can we admit Newton's conclusion and believe in absolute space? But it is not sufficient to state that all possible solutions are equally unpleasant to us. We must analyse in each case the reason of our dislike, in order to make our choice with the knowledge of the cause. The long discussion which follows must, therefore, be excused.

Let us resume our imaginary story. Thick clouds hide the stars from men who cannot observe them, and even are ignorant of their existence. How will those men know that the earth turns round? No doubt, for a longer period than did our ancestors, they will regard the soil on which they stand as fixed and immovable! They will wait a much longer time than we did for the coming of a Copernicus; but this Copernicus will come at last. How will he come? In the first place, the mechanical school of this world would not run their heads against an absolute contradiction. In the theory of relative motion we observe, besides real forces, two imaginary forces, which we call ordinary centrifugal force and compounded centrifugal force. Our imaginary scientists can thus explain everything by looking upon these two forces as real, and they would not see in this a contradiction of the generalised principle of inertia, for these forces would depend, the one on the relative positions of the different parts of the system, such as real attractions, and the other on their relative velocities, as in the case of real frictions. Many difficulties, however, would before long awaken their attention. If they succeeded in realising an isolated system, the centre of gravity of this system would not have an approximately rectilinear path. They could invoke, to explain this fact, the centrifugal forces which they would regard as real, and which, no doubt, they would attribute to the mutual actions of the bodies—only they would not see these forces vanish at great distances—that is to say, in proportion as the isolation is better realised. Far from it. Centrifugal force increases indefinitely with distance. Already this difficulty would seem to them sufficiently serious, but it would not detain them for long. They would soon imagine some very subtle

medium analogous to our ether, in which all
bodies would be bathed, and which would exercise on them a repulsive action.  But that is not
all.  Space is symmetrical—yet the laws of
motion would present no symmetry.  They should
be able to distinguish between right and left.
They would see, for instance, that cyclones always
turn in the same direction, while for reasons of
symmetry they should turn indifferently in any
direction.  If our scientists were able by dint of
much hard work to make their universe perfectly
symmetrical, this symmetry would not subsist,
although there is no apparent reason why it
should be disturbed in one direction more than
in another.  They would extract this from the
situation no doubt—they would invent something
which would not be more extraordinary than the
glass spheres of Ptolemy, and would thus go on
accumulating complications until the long-ex-
pected Copernicus would sweep them all away
with a single blow, saying it is much more simple
to admit that the earth turns round.  Just as
our Copernicus said to us: " It is more convenient
to suppose that the earth turns round, because the
laws of astronomy are thus expressed in a more
simple language," so he would say to them: " It
is more convenient to suppose that the earth turns
round, because the laws of mechanics are thus
expressed in much more simple language.  That
does not prevent absolute space—that is to say,
the point to which we must refer the earth to

know if it really does turn round—from having no objective existence.   And hence this affirmation: "the earth turns round," has no meaning, since it cannot be verified by experiment; since such an experiment not only cannot be realised or even dreamed of by the most daring Jules Verne, but cannot even be conceived of without contradiction; or, in other words, these two propositions, "the earth turns round," and, "it is more convenient to suppose that the earth turns round," have one and the same meaning.   There is nothing more in one than in the other.   Perhaps they will not be content with this, and may find it surprising that among all the hypotheses, or rather all the conventions, that can be made on this subject there is one which is more convenient than the rest?   But if we have admitted it without difficulty when it is a question of the laws of astronomy, why should we object when it is a question of the laws of mechanics?   We have seen that the co-ordinates of bodies are determined by differential equations of the second order, and that so are the differences of these co-ordinates.   This is what we have called the generalised principle of inertia, and the principle of relative motion.   If the distances of these bodies were determined in the same way by equations of the second order, it seems that the mind should be entirely satisfied.   How far does the mind receive this satisfaction, and why is it not content with it?   To explain this we had better take a simple example. I assume a system analogous to our solar system, but in which fixed stars foreign to this system cannot be perceived, so that astronomers can only observe the mutual distances of planets and the sun, and not the absolute longitudes of the planets. If we deduce directly from Newton's law the differential equations which define the variation of these distances, these equations will not be of the second order. I mean that if, outside Newton's law, we knew the initial values of these distances and of their derivatives with respect to time—that would not be sufficient to determine the values of these same distances at an ulterior moment. A datum would be still lacking, and this datum might be, for example, what astronomers call the area-constant. But here we may look at it from two different points of view. We may consider two kinds of constants. In the eyes of the physicist the world reduces to a series of phenomena depending, on the one hand, solely on initial phenomena, and, on the other hand, on the laws connecting consequence and antecedent. If observation then teaches us that a certain quantity is a constant, we shall have a choice of two ways of looking at it. So let us admit that there is a law which requires that this quantity shall not vary, but that by chance it has been found to have had in the beginning of time this value rather than that, a value that it has kept ever since. This quantity might then be called an *accidental* constant. Or again, let us

admit on the contrary that there is a law of nature
which imposes on this quantity this value and not
that.   We shall then have what may be called an
*essential* constant.   For example, in virtue of the
laws of Newton the duration of the revolution of
the earth must be constant.   But if it is 366 and
something sidereal days, and not 300 or 400, it is
because of some initial chance or other.   It is an
*accidental* constant.   If, on the other hand, the
exponent of the distance which figures in the
expression of the attractive force is equal to –2
and not to –3, it is not by chance, but because it
is required by Newton's law.   It is an *essential*
constant.   I do not know if this manner of giving
to chance its share is legitimate in itself, and if
there is not some artificiality about this distinction; but it is certain at least that in proportion
as Nature has secrets, she will be strictly arbitrary
and always uncertain in their application.   As far
as the area-constant is concerned, we are accustomed to look upon it as accidental.   Is it certain
that our imaginary astronomers would do the
same?   If they were able to compare two different
solar systems, they would get the idea that this
constant may assume several different values.   But
I supposed at the outset, as I was entitled to do,
that their system would appear isolated, and that
they would see no star which was foreign to their
system.   Under these conditions they could only
detect a single constant, which would have an
absolutely invariable, unique value.   They would

be led no doubt to look upon it as an essential constant.

One word in passing to forestall an objection. The inhabitants of this imaginary world could neither observe nor define the area-constant as we do, because absolute longitudes escape their notice; but that would not prevent them from being rapidly led to remark a certain constant which would be naturally introduced into their equations, and which would be nothing but what we call the area-constant. But then what would happen? If the area-constant is regarded as essential, as dependent upon a law of nature, then in order to calculate the distances of the planets at any given moment it would be sufficient to know the initial values of these distances and those of their first derivatives. From this new point of view, distances will be determined by differential equations of the second order. Would this completely satisfy the minds of these astronomers? I think not. In the first place, they would very soon see that in differentiating their equations so as to raise them to a higher order, these equations would become much more simple, and they would be especially struck by the difficulty which arises from symmetry. They would have to admit different laws, according as the aggregate of the planets presented the figure of a certain polyhedron or rather of a regular polyhedron, and these consequences can only be escaped by regarding the area-constant as accidental. I have taken this particular example, because I have imagined astronomers who would not be in the least concerned with terrestrial mechanics and whose vision would be bounded by the solar system. But our conclusions apply in all cases. Our universe is more extended than theirs, since we have fixed stars; but it, too, is very limited, so we might reason on the whole of our universe just as these astronomers do on their solar system. We thus see that we should be definitively led to conclude that the equations which define distances are of an order higher than the second. Why should this alarm us—why do we find it perfectly natural that the sequence of phenomena depends on initial values of the first derivatives of these distances, while we hesitate to admit that they may depend on the initial values of the second derivatives? It can only be because of mental habits created in us by the constant study of the generalised principle of inertia and of its consequences. The values of the distances at any given moment depend upon their initial values, on that of their first derivatives, and something else. What is that *something else?* If we do not want it to be merely one of the second derivatives, we have only the choice of hypotheses. Suppose, as is usually done, that this something else is the absolute orientation of the universe in space, or the rapidity with which this orientation varies; this may be, it certainly is, the most convenient solution for the geometer. But it is not the most satisfactory for the philosopher, because this orientation does not exist.  We may assume that this something else is the position or the velocity of some invisible body, and this is what is done by certain persons, who have even called the body Alpha, although we are destined to never know anything about this body except its name. This is an artifice entirely analogous to that of which I spoke at the end of the paragraph containing my reflections on the principle of inertia. But as a matter of fact the difficulty is artificial. Provided that the future indications of our instruments can only depend on the indications which they have given us, or that they might have formerly given us, such is all we want, and with these conditions we may rest satisfied.

# CHAPTER VIII.

## ENERGY AND THERMO-DYNAMICS.

*Energetics.*—The difficulties raised by the classical mechanics have led certain minds to prefer a new system which they call Energetics. Energetics took its rise in consequence of the discovery of the principle of the conservation of energy. Helmholtz gave it its definite form. We begin by defining two quantities which play a fundamental part in this theory. They are *kinetic energy*, or *vis viva*, and *potential energy*. Every change that the bodies of nature can undergo is regulated by two experimental laws. First, the sum of the kinetic and potential energies is constant. This is the principle of the conservation of energy. Second, if a system of bodies is at A at the time $t_o$, and at B at the time $t_1$, it always passes from the first position to the second by such a path that the *mean* value of the difference between the two kinds of energy in the interval of time which separates the two epochs $t_o$ and $t_1$ is a minimum. This is Hamilton's principle, and is one of the forms of the principle of least action. The energetic theory has the following advantages

over the classical. First, it is less incomplete—
that is to say, the principles of the conservation of
energy and of Hamilton teach us more than the
fundamental principles of the classical theory, and
exclude certain motions which do not occur in
nature and which would be compatible with the
classical theory. Second, it frees us from the
hypothesis of atoms, which it was almost impossible to avoid with the classical theory. But in
its turn it raises fresh difficulties. The definitions
of the two kinds of energy would raise difficulties
almost as great as those of force and mass in the
first system. However, we can get out of these
difficulties more easily, at any rate in the simplest
cases. Assume an isolated system formed of a
certain number of material points. Assume that
these points are acted upon by forces depending
only on their relative position and their distances apart, and independent of their velocities.
In virtue of the principle of the conservation of
energy there must be a function of forces. In this
simple case the enunciation of the principle of the
conservation of energy is of extreme simplicity.
A certain quantity, which may be determined by
experiment, must remain constant. This quantity
is the sum of two terms. The first depends only on
the position of the material points, and is independent of their velocities; the second is proportional to the squares of these velocities. This
decomposition can only take place in one way.
The first of these terms, which I shall call U, will

be potential energy; the second, which I shall call T, will be kinetic energy. It is true that if $T + U$ is constant, so is any function of $T + U$, $\phi (T + U)$. But this function $\phi (T + U)$ will not be the sum of two terms, the one independent of the velocities, and the other proportional to the square of the velocities. Among the functions which remain constant there is only one which enjoys this property. It is $T + U$ (or a linear function of $T + U$), it matters not which, since this linear function may always be reduced to $T + U$ by a change of unit and of origin. This, then, is what we call energy. The first term we shall call potential energy, and the second kinetic energy. The definition of the two kinds of energy may therefore be carried through without any ambiguity.

So it is with the definition of mass. Kinetic energy, or *vis viva*, is expressed very simply by the aid of the masses, and of the relative velocities of all the material points with reference to one of them. These relative velocities may be observed, and when we have the expression of the kinetic energy as a function of these relative velocities, the co-efficients of this expression will give us the masses. So in this simple case the fundamental ideas can be defined without difficulty. But the difficulties reappear in the more complicated cases if the forces, instead of depending solely on the distances, depend also on the velocities. For example, Weber supposes the mutual action of two electric molecules to depend not only on their

distance but on their velocity and on their acceleration. If material points attracted each other
according to an analogous law, U would depend
on the velocity, and it might contain a term
proportional to the square of the velocity. How
can we detect among such terms those that arise
from T or U? and how, therefore, can we distinguish the two parts of the energy? But there
is more than this. How can we define energy
itself? We have no more reason to take as our
definition $T + U$ rather than any other function of
$T + U$, when the property which characterised
$T + U$ has disappeared—namely, that of being the
sum of two terms of a particular form. But that
is not all. We must take account, not only of
mechanical energy properly so called, but of the
other forms of energy—heat, chemical energy,
electrical energy, etc. The principle of the conservation of energy must be written $T + U + Q =$
a constant, where T is the sensible kinetic energy,
U the potential energy of position, depending only
on the position of the bodies, Q the internal
molecular energy under the thermal, chemical, or
electrical form. This would be all right if the
three terms were absolutely distinct; if T were
proportional to the square of the velocities, U
independent of these velocities and of the state of
the bodies, Q independent of the velocities and of
the positions of the bodies, and depending only on
their internal state. The expression for the energy
could be decomposed in one way only into three

terms of this form. But this is not the case. Let us consider electrified bodies. The electro-static energy due to their mutual action will evidently depend on their charge—*i.e.*, on their state; but it will equally depend on their position. If these bodies are in motion, they will act electro-dynamically on one another, and the electro-dynamic energy will depend not only on their state and their position but on their velocities. We have therefore no means of making the selection of the terms which should form part of T, and U, and Q, and of separating the three parts of the energy. If T + U + Q is constant, the same is true of any function whatever, $\phi$ (T + U + Q).

If T + U + Q were of the particular form that I have suggested above, no ambiguity would ensue. Among the functions $\phi$ (T + U + Q) which remain constant, there is only one that would be of this particular form, namely the one which I would agree to call energy. But I have said this is not rigorously the case. Among the functions that remain constant there is not one which can rigorously be placed in this particular form. How then can we choose from among them that which should be called energy? We have no longer any guide in our choice.

Of the principle of the conservation of energy there is nothing left then but an enunciation:— *There is something which remains constant.* In this form it, in its turn, is outside the bounds of experiment and reduced to a kind of tautology. It is clear that if the world is governed by laws there will be quantities which remain constant. Like Newton's laws, and for an analogous reason, the principle of the conservation of energy being based on experiment, can no longer be invalidated by it.

This discussion shows that, in passing from the classical system to the energetic, an advance has been made; but it shows, at the same time, that we have not advanced far enough.

Another objection seems to be still more serious. The principle of least action is applicable to reversible phenomena, but it is by no means satisfactory as far as irreversible phenomena are concerned. Helmholtz attempted to extend it to this class of phenomena, but he did not and could not succeed. So far as this is concerned all has yet to be done. The very enunciation of the principle of least action is objectionable. To move from one point to another, a material molecule, acted upon by no force, but compelled to move on a surface, will take as its path the geodesic line—*i.e.*, the shortest path. This molecule seems to know the point to which we want to take it, to foresee the time that it will take it to reach it by such a path, and then to know how to choose the most convenient path. The enunciation of the principle presents it to us, so to speak, as a living and free entity. It is clear that it would be better to replace it by a less objectionable enunciation, one in which, as philosophers would say, final effects do not seem to be substituted for acting causes.

*Thermo-dynamics.*—The rôle of the two funda-mental principles of thermo-dynamics becomes daily more important in all branches of natural philosophy. Abandoning the ambitious theories of forty years ago, encumbered as they were with molecular hypotheses, we now try to rest on thermo-dynamics alone the entire edifice of mathematical physics. Will the two principles of Mayer and of Clausius assure to it founda-tions solid enough to last for some time? We all feel it, but whence does our confidence arise? An eminent physicist said to me one day, *àpropos* of the law of errors:—every one stoutly believes it, because mathematicians imagine that it is an effect of observation, and observers imagine that it is a mathematical theorem. And this was for a long time the case with the principle of the conservation of energy. It is no longer the same now. There is no one who does not know that it is an experimental fact. But then who gives us the right of attributing to the principle itself more generality and more precision than to the experi-ments which have served to demonstrate it? This is asking, if it is legitimate to generalise, as we do every day, empiric data, and I shall not be so foolhardy as to discuss this question, after so many philosophers have vainly tried to solve it. One thing alone is certain. If this permission were refused to us, science could not exist; or at least would be reduced to a kind of inventory, to the ascertaining of isolated facts. It would not longer be to us of any value, since it could not satisfy our need of order and harmony, and because it would be at the same time incapable of prediction. As the circumstances which have preceded any fact whatever will never again, in all probability, be simultaneously reproduced, we already require a first generalisation to predict whether the fact will be renewed as soon as the least of these circumstances is changed. But every proposition may be generalised in an infinite number of ways. Among all possible generalisations we must choose, and we cannot but choose the simplest. We are therefore led to adopt the same course as if a simple law were, other things being equal, more probable than a complex law. A century ago it was frankly confessed and proclaimed abroad that Nature loves simplicity; but Nature has proved the contrary since then on more than one occasion. We no longer confess this tendency, and we only keep of it what is indispensable, so that science may not become impossible. In formulating a general, simple, and formal law, based on a comparatively small number of not altogether consistent experiments, we have only obeyed a necessity from which the human mind cannot free itself. But there is something more, and that is why I dwell on this topic. No one doubts that Mayer's principle is not called upon to survive all the particular laws from which it was deduced, in

the same way that Newton's law has survived the
laws of Kepler from which it was derived, and
which are no longer anything but approximations,
if we take perturbations into account. Now why
does this principle thus occupy a kind of privileged
position among physical laws? There are many
reasons for that. At the outset we think that we
cannot reject it, or even doubt its absolute rigour,
without admitting the possibility of perpetual
motion; we certainly feel distrust at such a
prospect, and we believe ourselves less rash in
affirming it than in denying it. That perhaps is
not quite accurate. The impossibility of perpetual
motion only implies the conservation of energy for
reversible phenomena. The imposing simplicity
of Mayer's principle equally contributes to
strengthen our faith. In a law immediately deduced from experiments, such as Mariotte's law,
this simplicity would rather appear to us a reason
for distrust; but here this is no longer the case.
We take elements which at the first glance are
unconnected; these arrange themselves in an unexpected order, and form a harmonious whole.
We cannot believe that this unexpected harmony is a mere result of chance. Our conquest
appears to be valuable to us in proportion to the
efforts it has cost, and we feel the more certain of
having snatched its true secret from Nature in proportion as Nature has appeared more jealous of our
attempts to discover it. But these are only small
reasons. Before we raise Mayer's law to the

dignity of an absolute principle, a deeper discussion is necessary. But if we embark on this discussion we see that this absolute principle is not even easy to enunciate. In every particular case we clearly see what energy is, and we can give it at least a provisory definition; but it is impossible to find a general definition of it. If we wish to enunciate the principle in all its generality and apply it to the universe, we see it vanish, so to speak, and nothing is left but this—*there is something which remains constant*. But has this a meaning? In the determinist hypothesis the state of the universe is determined by an extremely large number $n$ of parameters, which I shall call $x_1, x_2, x_3 \ldots x_n$. As soon as we know at a given moment the values of these $n$ parameters, we also know their derivatives with respect to time, and we can therefore calculate the values of these same parameters at an anterior or ulterior moment. In other words, these $n$ parameters specify $n$ differential equations of the first order. These equations have $n-1$ integrals, and therefore there are $n-1$ functions of $x_1, x_2, x_3 \ldots x_n$, which remain constant. If we say then, *there is something which remains constant*, we are only enunciating a tautology. We would be even embarrassed to decide which among all our integrals is that which should retain the name of energy. Besides, it is not in this sense that Mayer's principle is understood when it is applied to a limited system. We admit, then, that $p$ of our $n$ parameters vary independently so that we have only $n-p$ relations, generally linear, between our $n$ parameters and their derivatives. Suppose, for the sake of simplicity, that the sum of the work done by the external forces is zero, as well as that of all the quantities of heat given off from the interior: what will then be the meaning of our principle? *There is a combination of these $n-p$ relations, of which the first member is an exact differential;* and then this differential vanishing in virtue of our $n-p$ relations, its integral is a constant, and it is this integral which we call energy. But how can it be that there are several parameters whose variations are independent? That can only take place in the case of external forces (although we have supposed, for the sake of simplicity, that the algebraical sum of all the work done by these forces has vanished). If, in fact, the system were completely isolated from all external action, the values of our $n$ parameters at a given moment would suffice to determine the state of the system at any ulterior moment whatever, provided that we still clung to the determinist hypothesis. We should therefore fall back on the same difficulty as before. If the future state of the system is not entirely determined by its present state, it is because it further depends on the state of bodies external to the system. But then, is it likely that there exist among the parameters $x$ which define the state of the system of equations independent of this state of the external bodies? and if in certain cases we think we can find them, is it not only because of our ignorance, and because the influence of these bodies is too weak for our experiment to be able to detect it? If the system is not regarded as completely isolated, it is probable that the rigorously exact expression of its internal energy will depend upon the state of the external bodies. Again, I have supposed above that the sum of all the external work is zero, and if we wish to be free from this rather artificial restriction the enunciation becomes still more difficult. To formulate Mayer's principle by giving it an absolute meaning, we must extend it to the whole universe, and then we find ourselves face to face with the very difficulty we have endeavoured to avoid. To sum up, and to use ordinary language, the law of the conservation of energy can have only one significance, because there is in it a property common to all possible properties; but in the determinist hypothesis there is only one possible, and then the law has no meaning. In the indeterminist hypothesis, on the other hand, it would have a meaning even if we wished to regard it in an absolute sense. It would appear as a limitation imposed on freedom.

But this word warns me that I am wandering from the subject, and that I am leaving the domain of mathematics and physics. I check myself, therefore, and I wish to retain only one impression of the whole of this discussion, and that is, that Mayer's law is a form subtle enough for us to be able to put into it almost anything we like. I do not mean by that that it corresponds to no objective reality, nor that it is reduced to mere tautology; since, in each particular case, and provided we do not wish to extend it to the absolute, it has a perfectly clear meaning. This subtlety is a reason for believing that it will last long; and as, on the other hand, it will only disappear to be blended in a higher harmony, we may work with confidence and utilise it, certain beforehand that our work will not be lost.

Almost everything that I have just said applies to the principle of Clausius. What distinguishes it is, that it is expressed by an inequality. It will be said perhaps that it is the same with all physical laws, since their precision is always limited by errors of observation. But they at least claim to be first approximations, and we hope to replace them little by little by more exact laws. If, on the other hand, the principle of Clausius reduces to an inequality, this is not caused by the imperfection of our means of observation, but by the very nature of the question.

*General Conclusions on Part III.*—The principles of mechanics are therefore presented to us under two different aspects. On the one hand, there are truths founded on experiment, and verified approximately as far as almost isolated systems are concerned; on the other hand,

there are postulates applicable to the whole of
the universe and regarded as rigorously true.
If these postulates possess a generality and a
certainty which falsify the experimental truths
from which they were deduced, it is because
they reduce in final analysis to a simple convention that we have a right to make, because
we are certain beforehand that no experiment
can contradict it.  This convention, however, is
not absolutely arbitrary; it is not the child
of our caprice.  We admit it because certain
experiments have shown us that it will be convenient, and thus is explained how experiment
has built up the principles of mechanics, and
why, moreover, it cannot reverse them.  Take a
comparison with geometry.  The fundamental
propositions of geometry, for instance, Euclid's
postulate, are only conventions, and it is quite
as unreasonable to ask if they are true or false
as to ask if the metric system is true or false.
Only, these conventions are convenient, and there
are certain experiments which prove it to us.   At
the first glance, the analogy is complete, the rôle
of experiment seems the same.   We shall therefore be tempted to say, either mechanics must
be looked upon as experimental science and then
it should be the same with geometry; or, on the
contrary, geometry is a deductive science, and
then we can say the same of mechanics.  Such
a conclusion would be illegitimate.  The experiments which have led us to adopt as more

convenient the fundamental conventions of geometry refer to bodies which have nothing in common with those that are studied by geometry. They refer to the properties of solid bodies and to the propagation of light in a straight line. These are mechanical, optical experiments. In no way can they be regarded as geometrical experiments. And even the probable reason why our geometry seems convenient to us is, that our bodies, our hands, and our limbs enjoy the properties of solid bodies. Our fundamental experiments are pre-eminently physiological experiments which refer, not to the space which is the object that geometry must study, but to our body—that is to say, to the instrument which we use for that study. On the other hand, the fundamental conventions of mechanics and the experiments which prove to us that they are convenient, certainly refer to the same objects or to analogous objects. Conventional and general principles are the natural and direct generalisations of experimental and particular principles. Let it not be said that I am thus tracing artificial frontiers between the sciences; that I am separating by a barrier geometry properly so called from the study of solid bodies. I might just as well raise a barrier between experimental mechanics and the conventional mechanics of general principles. Who does not see, in fact, that by separating these two sciences we mutilate both, and that what will remain of the conventional mechanics when it is isolated will be but very little, and can in no way be compared with that grand body of doctrine which is called geometry.

We now understand why the teaching of mechanics should remain experimental. Thus only can we be made to understand the genesis of the science, and that is indispensable for a complete knowledge of the science itself. Besides, if we study mechanics, it is in order to apply it; and we can only apply it if it remains objective. Now, as we have seen, when principles gain in generality and certainty they lose in objectivity. It is therefore especially with the objective side of principles that we must be early familiarised, and this can only be by passing from the particular to the general, instead of from the general to the particular.

Principles are conventions and definitions in disguise. They are, however, deduced from experimental laws, and these laws have, so to speak, been erected into principles to which our mind attributes an absolute value. Some philosophers have generalised far too much. They have thought that the principles were the whole of science, and therefore that the whole of science was conventional. This paradoxical doctrine, which is called Nominalism, cannot stand examination. How can a law become a principle? It expressed a relation between two real terms, A and B; but it was not rigorously true, it was only approximate. We introduce arbitrarily an intermediate term, C, more or less imaginary, and C is *by definition* that which has with A *exactly* the relation expressed by the law. So our law is decomposed into an absolute and rigorous principle which expresses the relation of A to C, and an approximate experimental and revisable law which expresses the relation of C to B. But it is clear that however far this decomposition may be carried, laws will always remain. We shall now enter into the domain of laws properly so called.

# PART IV.

## *NATURE.*

## CHAPTER IX.

### HYPOTHESES IN PHYSICS.

*The Rôle of Experiment and Generalisation.*—
Experiment is the sole source of truth. It alone
can teach us something new; it alone can give
us certainty. These are two points that cannot
be questioned. But then, if experiment is everything, what place is left for mathematical physics?
What can experimental physics do with such an
auxiliary—an auxiliary, moreover, which seems
useless, and even may be dangerous?

However, mathematical physics exists. It has
rendered undeniable service, and that is a fact
which has to be explained. It is not sufficient
merely to observe; we must use our observations,
and for that purpose we must generalise. This
is what has always been done, only as the recollection of past errors has made man more and more
circumspect, he has observed more and more and
generalised less and less. Every age has scoffed
at its predecessor, accusing it of having generalised

too boldly and too naïvely. Descartes used to commiserate the Ionians. Descartes in his turn makes us smile, and no doubt some day our children will laugh at us. Is there no way of getting at once to the gist of the matter, and thereby escaping the raillery which we foresee? Cannot we be content with experiment alone? No, that is impossible; that would be a complete misunderstanding of the true character of science. The man of science must work with method. Science is built up of facts, as a house is built of stones; but an accumulation of facts is no more a science than a heap of stones is a house. Most important of all, the man of science must exhibit foresight. Carlyle has written somewhere something after this fashion. " Nothing but facts are of importance. John Lackland passed by here. Here is something that is admirable. Here is a reality for which I would give all the theories in the world."[1] Carlyle was a compatriot of Bacon, and, like him, he wished to proclaim his worship of *the God of Things as they are.*

But Bacon would not have said that. That is the language of the historian. The physicist would most likely have said: " John Lackland passed by here. It is all the same to me, for he will not pass this way again."

We all know that there are good and bad experiments. The latter accumulate in vain. Whether there are a hundred or a thousand,

[1] V. *Past and Present*, end of Chapter I., Book II.—[TR.]

one single piece of work by a real master—by a Pasteur, for example—will be sufficient to sweep them into oblivion. Bacon would have thoroughly understood that, for he invented the phrase *experimentum crucis;* but Carlyle would not have understood it. A fact is a fact. A student has read such and such a number on his thermometer. He has taken no precautions. It does not matter; he has read it, and if it is only the fact which counts, this is a reality that is as much entitled to be called a reality as the peregrinations of King John Lackland. What, then, is a good experiment? It is that which teaches us something more than an isolated fact. It is that which enables us to predict, and to generalise. Without generalisation, prediction is impossible. The circumstances under which one has operated will never again be reproduced simultaneously. The fact observed will never be repeated. All that can be affirmed is that under analogous circumstances an analogous fact will be produced. To predict it, we must therefore invoke the aid of analogy—that is to say, even at this stage, we must generalise. However timid we may be, there must be interpolation. Experiment only gives us a certain number of isolated points. They must be connected by a continuous line, and this is a true generalisation. But more is done. The curve thus traced will pass between and near the points observed; it will not pass through the points themselves. Thus we are not restricted to generalising our experiment, we correct it; and the physicist who would abstain from these corrections, and really content himself with experiment pure and simple, would be compelled to enunciate very extra-ordinary laws indeed. Detached facts cannot therefore satisfy us, and that is why our science must be ordered, or, better still, generalised.

It is often said that experiments should be made without preconceived ideas. That is impossible. Not only would it make every experiment fruitless, but even if we wished to do so, it could not be done. Every man has his own conception of the world, and this he cannot so easily lay aside. We must, for example, use language, and our language is necessarily steeped in preconceived ideas. Only they are unconscious preconceived ideas, which are a thousand times the most dangerous of all. Shall we say, that if we cause others to intervene of which we are fully conscious, that we shall only aggravate the evil? I do not think so. I am inclined to think that they will serve as ample counterpoises—I was almost going to say antidotes. They will generally disagree, they will enter into conflict one with another, and *ipso facto*, they will force us to look at things under different aspects. This is enough to free us. He is no longer a slave who can choose his master.

Thus, by generalisation, every fact observed enables us to predict a large number of others; only, we ought not to forget that the first alone is certain, and that all the others are merely probable. However solidly founded a prediction may appear to us, we are never *absolutely* sure that experiment will not prove it to be baseless if we set to work to verify it. But the probability of its accuracy is often so great that practically we may be content with it. It is far better to predict without certainty, than never to have predicted at all. We should never, therefore, disdain to verify when the opportunity presents itself. But every experiment is long and difficult, and the labourers are few, and the number of facts which we require to predict is enormous; and besides this mass, the number of direct verifications that we can make will never be more than a negligible quantity. Of this little that we can directly attain we must choose the best. Every experiment must enable us to make a maximum number of predictions having the highest possible degree of probability. The problem is, so to speak, to increase the output of the scientific machine. I may be permitted to compare science to a library which must go on increasing indefinitely; the librarian has limited funds for his purchases, and he must, therefore, strain every nerve not to waste them. Experimental physics has to make the purchases, and experimental physics alone can enrich the library. As for mathematical physics, her duty is to draw up the catalogue. If the catalogue is well done the library is none the richer for it; but the reader will be enabled to utilise its riches; and also by showing the librarian the gaps in his collection, it will help him to make a judicious use of his funds, which is all the more important, inasmuch as those funds are entirely inadequate. That is the rôle of mathematical physics. It must direct generalisation, so as to increase what I called just now the output of science. By what means it does this, and how it may do it without danger, is what we have now to examine.

*The Unity of Nature.*—Let us first of all observe that every generalisation supposes in a certain measure a belief in the unity and simplicity of Nature. As far as the unity is concerned, there can be no difficulty. If the different parts of the universe were not as the organs of the same body, they would not re-act one upon the other; they would mutually ignore each other, and we in particular should only know one part. We need not, therefore, ask if Nature is one, but how she is one.

As for the second point, that is not so clear. It is not certain that Nature is simple. Can we without danger act as if she were?

There was a time when the simplicity of Mariotte's law was an argument in favour of its accuracy: when Fresnel himself, after having said in a conversation with Laplace that Nature cares naught for analytical difficulties, was compelled to explain his words so as not to give offence to current opinion. Nowadays, ideas have changed considerably; but those who do not believe that natural laws must be simple, are still often obliged to act as if they did believe it. They cannot entirely dispense with this necessity without making all generalisation, and therefore all science, impossible. It is clear that any fact can be generalised in an infinite number of ways, and it is a question of choice. The choice can only be guided by considerations of simplicity. Let us take the most ordinary case, that of interpolation. We draw a continuous line as regularly as possible between the points given by observation. Why do we avoid angular points and inflexions that are too sharp? Why do we not make our curve describe the most capricious zigzags? It is because we know beforehand, or think we know, that the law we have to express cannot be so complicated as all that. The mass of Jupiter may be deduced either from the movements of his satellites, or from the perturbations of the major planets, or from those of the minor planets. If we take the mean of the determinations obtained by these three methods, we find three numbers very close together, but not quite identical. This result might be interpreted by supposing that the gravitation constant is not the same in the three cases; the observations would be certainly much better represented. Why do we reject this interpretation? Not because it is absurd, but because it is uselessly complicated. We shall only accept it when we are forced to, and it is not imposed upon us yet. To sum up, in most cases every law is held to be simple until the contrary is proved.

This custom is imposed upon physicists by the reasons that I have indicated, but how can it be justified in the presence of discoveries which daily show us fresh details, richer and more complex? How can we even reconcile it with the unity of nature? For if all things are interdependent, the relations in which so many different objects intervene can no longer be simple.

If we study the history of science we see produced two phenomena which are, so to speak, each the inverse of the other. Sometimes it is simplicity which is hidden under what is apparently complex; sometimes, on the contrary, it is simplicity which is apparent, and which conceals extremely complex realities. What is there more complicated than the disturbed motions of the planets, and what more simple than Newton's law? There, as Fresnel said, Nature playing with analytical difficulties, only uses simple means, and creates by their combination I know not what tangled skein. Here it is the hidden simplicity which must be disentangled. Examples to the contrary abound. In the kinetic theory of gases, molecules of tremendous velocity are discussed, whose paths, deformed by incessant impacts, have the most capricious shapes, and plough their way through space in every direction. The result observable is Mariotte's simple law. Each individual fact was complicated. The law of great numbers has re-established simplicity in the mean. Here the simplicity is only apparent,

and the coarseness of our senses alone prevents us
from seeing the complexity.

Many phenomena obey a law of proportionality. But why? Because in these phenomena
there is something which is very small. The
simple law observed is only the translation of
the general analytical rule by which the infinitely
small increment of a function is proportional
to the increment of the variable. As in reality
our increments are not infinitely small, but only
very small, the law of proportionality is only
approximate, and simplicity is only apparent.
What I have just said applies to the law of the
superposition of small movements, which is so
fruitful in its applications and which is the foundation of optics.

And Newton's law itself? Its simplicity, so
long undetected, is perhaps only apparent. Who
knows if it be not due to some complicated
mechanism, to the impact of some subtle matter
animated by irregular movements, and if it has
not become simple merely through the play of
averages and large numbers? In any case, it
is difficult not to suppose that the true law contains complementary terms which may become
sensible at small distances. If in astronomy they
are negligible, and if the law thus regains its
simplicity, it is solely on account of the enormous
distances of the celestial bodies. No doubt, if our
means of investigation became more and more
penetrating, we should discover the simple beneath

the complex, and then the complex from the simple, and then again the simple beneath the complex, and so on, without ever being able to predict what the last term will be. We must stop somewhere, and for science to be possible we must stop where we have found simplicity. That is the only ground on which we can erect the edifice of our generalisations. But, this simplicity being only apparent, will the ground be solid enough? That is what we have now to discover.

For this purpose let us see what part is played in our generalisations by the belief in simplicity. We have verified a simple law in a considerable number of particular cases. We refuse to admit that this coincidence, so often repeated, is a result of mere chance, and we conclude that the law must be true in the general case.

Kepler remarks that the positions of a planet observed by Tycho are all on the same ellipse. Not for one moment does he think that, by a singular freak of chance, Tycho had never looked at the heavens except at the very moment when the path of the planet happened to cut that ellipse. What does it matter then if the simplicity be real or if it hide a complex truth? Whether it be due to the influence of great numbers which reduces individual differences to a level, or to the greatness or the smallness of certain quantities which allow of certain terms to be neglected—in no case is it due to chance. This simplicity, real or apparent, has always a cause. We shall therefore always be able to reason in the same fashion, and if a simple law has been observed in several particular cases, we may legitimately suppose that it still will be true in analogous cases. To refuse to admit this would be to attribute an inadmissible rôle to chance. However, there is a difference. If the simplicity were real and profound it would bear the test of the increasing precision of our methods of measurement. If, then, we believe Nature to be profoundly simple. we must conclude that it is an approximate and not a rigorous simplicity. This is what was formerly done, but it is what we have no longer the right to do. The simplicity of Kepler's laws, for instance, is only apparent; but that does not prevent them from being applied to almost all systems analogous to the solar system, though that prevents them from being rigorously exact.

*Rôle of Hypothesis.*—Every generalisation is a hypothesis. Hypothesis therefore plays a necessary rôle, which no one has ever contested. Only, it should always be as soon as possible submitted to verification. It goes without saying that, if it cannot stand this test, it must be abandoned without any hesitation. This is, indeed, what is generally done; but sometimes with a certain impatience. Ah well! this impatience is not justified. The physicist who has just given up one of his hypotheses should, on the contrary, rejoice, for he found an unexpected opportunity of discovery. His hypothesis, I imagine, had not been lightly adopted. It took into account all the known factors which seem capable of intervention in the phenomenon. If it is not verified, it is because there is something unexpected and extraordinary about it, because we are on the point of finding something unknown and new. Has the hypothesis thus rejected been sterile? Far from it. It may be even said that it has rendered more service than a true hypothesis. Not only has it been the occasion of a decisive experiment, but if this experiment had been made by chance, without the hypothesis, no conclusion could have been drawn; nothing extraordinary would have been seen; and only one fact the more would have been catalogued, without deducing from it the remotest consequence.

Now, under what conditions is the use of hypothesis without danger? The proposal to submit all to experiment is not sufficient. Some hypotheses are dangerous, — first and foremost those which are tacit and unconscious. And since we make them without knowing them, we cannot get rid of them. Here again, there is a service that mathematical physics may render us. By the precision which is its characteristic, we are compelled to formulate all the hypotheses that we would unhesitatingly make without its aid. Let us also notice that it is important not to multiply hypotheses indefinitely. If we construct a theory based upon multiple hypotheses, and if experiment condemns it, which of the premisses must be changed? It is impossible to tell. Conversely, if the experiment succeeds, must we suppose that it has verified all these hypotheses at once? Can several unknowns be determined from a single equation?

We must also take care to distinguish between the different kinds of hypotheses. First of all, there are those which are quite natural and necessary. It is difficult not to suppose that the influence of very distant bodies is quite negligible, that small movements obey a linear law, and that effect is a continuous function of its cause. I will say as much for the conditions imposed by symmetry. All these hypotheses affirm, so to speak, the common basis of all the theories of mathematical physics. They are the last that should be abandoned. There is a second category of hypotheses which I shall qualify as indifferent. In most questions the analyst assumes, at the beginning of his calculations, either that matter is continuous, or the reverse, that it is formed of atoms. In either case, his results would have been the same. On the atomic supposition he has a little more difficulty in obtaining them—that is all. If, then, experiment confirms his conclusions, will he suppose that he has proved, for example, the real existence of atoms?

In optical theories two vectors are introduced, one of which we consider as a velocity and the other as a vortex. This again is an indifferent hypothesis, since we should have arrived at the same conclusions by assuming the former to be a vortex and the latter to be a velocity. The success of the experiment cannot prove, therefore, that the first vector is really a velocity. It only proves one thing—namely, that it is a vector; and that is the only hypothesis that has really been introduced into the premisses. To give it the concrete appearance that the fallibility of our minds demands, it was necessary to consider it either as a velocity or as a vortex. In the same way, it was necessary to represent it by an $x$ or a $y$, but the result will not prove that we were right or wrong in regarding it as a velocity; nor will it prove we are right or wrong in calling it $x$ and not $y$.

These indifferent hypotheses are never dangerous provided their characters are not misunderstood. They may be useful, either as artifices for calculation, or to assist our understanding by concrete images, to fix the ideas, as we say. They need not therefore be rejected. The hypotheses of the third category are real generalisations. They must be confirmed or invalidated by experiment. Whether verified or condemned, they will always be fruitful; but, for the reasons I have given, they will only be so if they are not too numerous.

*Origin of Mathematical Physics.*—Let us go further and study more closely the conditions which have assisted the development of mathematical physics. We recognise at the outset that

the efforts of men of science have always tended
to resolve the complex phenomenon given directly
by experiment into a very large number of elementary phenomena, and that in three different
ways.

First, with respect to time. Instead of embracing
in its entirety the progressive development of a
phenomenon, we simply try to connect each
moment with the one immediately preceding.
We admit that the present state of the world
only depends on the immediate past, without
being directly influenced, so to speak, by the
recollection of a more distant past. Thanks to
this postulate, instead of studying directly the
whole succession of phenomena, we may confine
ourselves to writing down its *differential equation;*
for the laws of Kepler we substitute the law of
Newton.

Next, we try to decompose the phenomena in
space. What experiment gives us is a confused
aggregate of facts spread over a scene of considerable extent. We must try to deduce the elementary phenomenon, which will still be localised in a
very small region of space.

A few examples perhaps will make my meaning
clearer. If we wished to study in all its complexity the distribution of temperature in a cooling
solid, we could never do so. This is simply because, if we only reflect that a point in the solid
can directly impart some of its heat to a neighbouring point, it will immediately impart that

heat only to the nearest points, and it is but gradually that the flow of heat will reach other portions of the solid. The elementary phenomenon is the interchange of heat between two contiguous points. It is strictly localised and relatively simple if, as is natural, we admit that it is not influenced by the temperature of the molecules whose distance apart is small.

I bend a rod: it takes a very complicated form, the direct investigation of which would be impossible. But I can attack the problem, however, if I notice that its flexure is only the resultant of the deformations of the very small elements of the rod, and that the deformation of each of these elements only depends on the forces which are directly applied to it, and not in the least on those which may be acting on the other elements.

In all these examples, which may be increased without difficulty, it is admitted that there is no action at a distance or at great distances. That is an hypothesis. It is not always true, as the law of gravitation proves. It must therefore be verified. If it is confirmed, even approximately, it is valuable, for it helps us to use mathematical physics, at any rate by successive approximations. If it does not stand the test, we must seek something else that is analogous, for there are other means of arriving at the elementary phenomenon. If several bodies act simultaneously, it may happen that their actions are independent, and may be added one to the other. either as vectors or as scalar quantities. The elementary phenomenon is then the action of an isolated body. Or suppose, again, it is a question of small movements, or more generally of small variations which obey the well-known law of mutual or relative independence. The movement observed will then be decomposed into simple movements—for example, sound into its harmonics, and white light into its monochromatic components. When we have discovered in which direction to seek for the elementary phenomena, by what means may we reach it ? First, it will often happen that in order to predict it, or rather in order to predict what is useful to us, it will not be necessary to know its mechanism. The law of great numbers will suffice. Take for example the propagation of heat. Each molecule radiates towards its neighbour—we need not inquire according to what law; and if we make any supposition in this respect, it will be an indifferent hypothesis, and therefore useless and unverifiable. In fact, by the action of averages and thanks to the symmetry of the medium, all differences are levelled, and, whatever the hypothesis may be, the result is always the same.

The same feature is presented in the theory of elasticity, and in that of capillarity. The neighbouring molecules attract and repel each other, we need not inquire by what law. It is enough for us that this attraction is sensible at small distances only, and that the molecules are very numerous, that the medium is symmetrical, and we have only to let the law of great numbers come into play.

Here again the simplicity of the elementary phenomenon is hidden beneath the complexity of the observable resultant phenomenon; but in its turn this simplicity was only apparent and disguised a very complex mechanism.  Evidently the best means of reaching the elementary phenomenon would be experiment.  It would be necessary by experimental artifices to dissociate the complex system which nature offers for our investigations and carefully to study the elements as dissociated as possible; for example, natural white light would be decomposed into monochromatic lights by the aid of the prism, and into polarised lights by the aid of the polariser.  Unfortunately, that is neither always possible nor always sufficient, and sometimes the mind must run ahead of experiment.  I shall only give one example which has always struck me rather forcibly.  If I decompose white light, I shall be able to isolate a portion of the spectrum, but however small it may be, it will always be a certain width.  In the same way the natural lights which are called *monochromatic* give us a very fine array, but a y which is not, however, infinitely fine.  It might be supposed that in the experimental study of the properties of these natural lights, by operating with finer and finer rays, and passing on at last to the limit, so to speak, we should eventually obtain the properties of a rigorously monochromatic light. That would not be accurate. I assume that two rays emanate from the same source, that they are first polarised in planes at right angles, that they are then brought back again to the same plane of polarisation, and that we try to obtain interference. If the light were *rigorously* monochromatic, there would be interference; but with our nearly monochromatic lights, there will be no interference, and that, however narrow the ray may be. For it to be otherwise, the ray would have to be several million times finer than the finest known rays.

Here then we should be led astray by proceeding to the limit. The mind has to run ahead of the experiment, and if it has done so with success, it is because it has allowed itself to be guided by the instinct of simplicity. The knowledge of the elementary fact enables us to state the problem in the form of an equation. It only remains to deduce from it by combination the observable and verifiable complex fact. That is what we call *integration,* and it is the province of the mathematician. It might be asked, why in physical science generalisation so readily takes the mathematical form. The reason is now easy to see. It is not only because we have to express numerical laws; it is because the observable phenomenon is due to the superposition of a large number of elementary phenomena which are *all similar to each other;* and in this way differential equations are quite naturally introduced. It is

not enough that each elementary phenomenon
should obey simple laws: all those that we have
to combine must obey the same law; then only
is the intervention of mathematics of any use.
Mathematics teaches us, in fact, to combine like
with like.   Its object is to divine the result of a
combination without having to reconstruct that
combination element by element.   If we have to
repeat the same operation several times, mathematics enables us to avoid this repetition by telling
the result beforehand by a kind of induction.
This I have explained before in the chapter on
mathematical reasoning.   But for that purpose
all these operations must be similar; in the contrary case we must evidently make up our minds
to working them out in full one after the other,
and mathematics will be useless.   It is therefore,
thanks to the approximate homogeneity of the
matter studied by physicists, that mathematical
physics came into existence.   In the natural
sciences the following conditions are no longer to
be found:—homogeneity, relative independence of
remote parts, simplicity of the elementary fact;
and that is why the student of natural science is
compelled to have recourse to other modes of
generalisation.

# CHAPTER X.

## THE THEORIES OF MODERN PHYSICS.

*Significance of Physical Theories.*—The ephemeral nature of scientific theories takes by surprise the man of the world.   Their brief period of prosperity ended, he sees them abandoned one after another; he sees ruins piled upon ruins; he predicts that the theories in fashion to-day will in a short time succumb in their turn, and he concludes that they are absolutely in vain.   This is what he calls the *bankruptcy of science.*

His scepticism is superficial; he does not take into account the object of scientific theories and the part they play, or he would understand that the ruins may be still good for something. No theory seemed established on firmer ground than Fresnel's, which attributed light to the movements of the ether.   Then if Maxwell's theory is to-day preferred, does that mean that Fresnel's work was in vain?   No; for Fresnel's object was not to know whether there really is an ether, if it is or is not formed of atoms, if these atoms really move in this way or that; his object was to predict optical phenomena.

This Fresnel's theory enables us to do to-day as well as it did before Maxwell's time.   The differential equations are always true, they may be always integrated by the same methods, and the results of this integration still preserve their value.   It cannot be said that this is reducing physical theories to simple practical recipes; these equations express relations, and if the equations remain true, it is because the relations preserve their reality.   They teach us now, as they did then, that there is such and such a relation between this thing and that; only, the something which we then called *motion*, we now call *electric current*.   But these are merely names of the images we substituted for the real objects which Nature will hide for ever from our eyes.   The true relations between these real objects are the only reality we can attain, and the sole condition is that the same relations shall exist between these objects as between the images we are forced to put in their place.   If the relations are known to us, what does it matter if we think it convenient to replace one image by another ?

That a given periodic phenomenon (an electric oscillation, for instance) is really due to the vibration of a given atom, which, behaving like a pendulum, is really displaced in this manner or that, all this is neither certain nor essential. But that there is between the electric oscillation, the movement of the pendulum, and all periodic phenomena an intimate relationship which corresponds to a profound reality; that this relationship,

this similarity, or rather this parallelism, is con
tinued in the details; that it is a consequence of
more general principles such as that of the conservation of energy, and that of least action; this
we may affirm; this is the truth which will ever
remain the same in whatever garb we may see fit
to clothe it.

Many theories of dispersion have been proposed.
The first were imperfect, and contained but little
truth. Then came that of Helmholtz, and this
in its turn was modified in different ways; its
author himself conceived another theory, founded
on Maxwell's principles. But the remarkable
thing is, that all the scientists who followed
Helmholtz obtain the same equations, although
their starting-points were to all appearance widely
separated. I venture to say that these theories
are all simultaneously true; not merely because
they express a true relation—that between absorption and abnormal dispersion. In the premisses
of these theories the part that is true is the part
common to all: it is the affirmation of this or
that relation between certain things, which some
call by one name and some by another.

The kinetic theory of gases has given rise to
many objections, to which it would be difficult
to find an answer were it claimed that the theory
is absolutely true. But all these objections do
not alter the fact that it has been useful,
particularly in revealing to us one true relation
which would otherwise have remained profoundly

hidden—the relation between gaseous and osmotic pressures. In this sense, then, it may be said to be true.

When a physicist finds a contradiction between two theories which are equally dear to him, he sometimes says: "Let us not be troubled, but let us hold fast to the two ends of the chain, lest we lose the intermediate links." This argument of the embarrassed theologian would be ridiculous if we were to attribute to physical theories the interpretation given them by the man of the world. In case of contradiction one of them at least should be considered false. But this is no longer the case if we only seek in them what should be sought. It is quite possible that they both express true relations, and that the contradictions only exist in the images we have formed to ourselves of reality. To those who feel that we are going too far in our limitations of the domain accessible to the scientist, I reply: These questions which we forbid you to investigate, and which you so regret, are not only insoluble, they are illusory and devoid of meaning.

Such a philosopher claims that all physics can be explained by the mutual impact of atoms. If he simply means that the same relations obtain between physical phenomena as between the mutual impact of a large number of billiard balls—well and good! this is verifiable, and perhaps is true. But he means something more, and we think we understand him, because we think we know what an impact is. Why? Simply because we have often watched a game of billiards. Are we to understand that God experiences the same sensations in the contemplation of His work that we do in watching a game of billiards? If it is not our intention to give his assertion this fantastic meaning, and if we do not wish to give it the more restricted meaning I have already mentioned, which is the sound meaning, then it has no meaning at all. Hypotheses of this kind have therefore only a metaphorical sense. The scientist should no more banish them than a poet banishes metaphor; but he ought to know what they are worth. They may be useful to give satisfaction to the mind, and they will do no harm as long as they are only indifferent hypotheses.

These considerations explain to us why certain theories, that were thought to be abandoned and definitively condemned by experiment, are suddenly revived from their ashes and begin a new life. It is because they expressed true relations, and had not ceased to do so when for some reason or other we felt it necessary to enunciate the same relations in another language. Their life had been latent, as it were.

Barely fifteen years ago, was there anything more ridiculous, more quaintly old-fashioned, than the fluids of Coulomb? And yet, here they are re-appearing under the name of *electrons*. In what do these permanently electrified molecules differ from the electric molecules of Coulomb? It is true that in the electrons the electricity is supported by a little, a very little matter; in other words, they have mass. Yet Coulomb did not deny mass to his fluids, or if he did, it was with reluctance. It would be rash to affirm that the belief in electrons will not also undergo an eclipse, but it was none the less curious to note this unexpected renaissance.

But the most striking example is Carnot's principle. Carnot established it, starting from false hypotheses. When it was found that heat was indestructible, and may be converted into work, his ideas were completely abandoned; later, Clausius returned to them, and to him is due their definitive triumph. In its primitive form, Carnot's theory expressed in addition to true relations, other inexact relations, the *débris* of old ideas; but the presence of the latter did not alter the reality of the others. Clausius had only to separate them, just as one lops off dead branches.

The result was the second fundamental law of thermodynamics. The relations were always the same, although they did not hold, at least to all appearance, between the same objects. This was sufficient for the principle to retain its value. Nor have the reasonings of Carnot perished on this account; they were applied to an imperfect conception of matter, but their form—*i.e.*, the essential part of them, remained correct. What

I have just said throws some light at the same
time on the rôle of general principles, such as
those of the principle of least action or of the
conservation of energy. These principles are of
very great value. They were obtained in the
search for what there was in common in the
enunciation of numerous physical laws; they
thus represent the quintessence of innumerable
observations. However, from their very generality
results a consequence to which I have called
attention in Chapter VIII.—namely, that they are
no longer capable of verification. As we cannot
give a general definition of energy, the principle
of the conservation of energy simply signifies that
there is a *something* which remains constant.
Whatever fresh notions of the world may be
given us by future experiments, we are certain
beforehand that there is something which remains
constant, and which may be called *energy*. Does
this mean that the principle has no meaning and
vanishes into a tautology? Not at all. It means
that the different things to which we give the
name of *energy* are connected by a true relationship; it affirms between them a real relation.
But then, if this principle has a meaning, it may
be false; it may be that we have no right to
extend indefinitely its applications, and yet it is
certain beforehand to be verified in the strict
sense of the word. How, then, shall we know
when it has been extended as far as is legitimate?
Simply when it ceases to be useful to us—*i.e.*,

when we can no longer use it to predict correctly new phenomena. We shall be certain in such a case that the relation affirmed is no longer real, for otherwise it would be fruitful; experiment without directly contradicting a new extension of the principle will nevertheless have condemned it.

*Physics and Mechanism.*—Most theorists have a constant· predilection for explanations borrowed from physics, mechanics, or dynamics. Some would be satisfied if they could account for all phenomena by the motion of molecules attracting one another according to certain laws. Others are more exact; they would suppress attractions acting at a distance; their molecules would follow rectilinear paths, from which they would only be deviated by impacts. Others again, such as Hertz, suppress the forces as well, but suppose their molecules subjected to geometrical connections analogous, for instance, to those of articulated systems; thus, they wish to reduce dynamics to a kind of kinematics. In a word, they all wish to bend nature into a certain form, and unless they can do this they cannot be satisfied. Is Nature flexible enough for this?

We shall examine this question in Chapter XII., *àpropos* of Maxwell's theory. Every time that the principles of least action and energy are satisfied, we shall see that not only is there always a mechanical explanation possible, but that there is an unlimited number of such explanations. By means of a well-known theorem due to Königs,

it may be shown that we can explain everything
in an unlimited number of ways, by connections
after the manner of Hertz, or, again, by central
forces. No doubt it may be just as easily demonstrated that everything may be explained by
simple impacts. For this, let us bear in mind
that it is not enougn to be content with the
ordinary matter of which we are aware by means
of our senses, and the movements of which we
observe directly. We may conceive of ordinary
matter as either composed of atoms, whose internal
movements escape us, our senses being able to
estimate only the displacement of the whole; or
we may imagine one of those subtle fluids, which
under the name of *ether* or other names, have
from all time played so important a rôle in
physical theories. Often we go further, and regard
the ether as the only primitive, or even as the
only true matter. The more moderate consider
ordinary matter to be condensed ether, and
there is nothing startling in this conception; but
others only reduce its importance still further,
and see in matter nothing more than the geometrical locus of singularities in the ether. Lord
Kelvin, for instance, holds what we call matter
to be only the locus of those points at which the
ether is animated by vortex motions. Riemann
believes it to be locus of those points at which
ether is constantly destroyed; to Wiechert or
Larmor, it is the locus of the points at which
the ether has undergone a kind of torsion of a

very particular kind. Taking any one of these points of view, I ask by what right do we apply to the ether the mechanical properties observed in ordinary matter, which is but false matter? The ancient fluids, caloric, electricity, etc., were abandoned when it was seen that heat is not indestructible. But they were also laid aside for another reason. In materialising them, their individuality was, so to speak, emphasised—gaps were opened between them; and these gaps had to be filled in when the sentiment of the unity of Nature became stronger, and when the intimate relations which connect all the parts were perceived. In multiplying the fluids, not only did the ancient physicists create unnecessary entities, but they destroyed real ties. It is not enough for a theory not to affirm false relations; it must not conceal true relations.

Does our ether actually exist? We know the origin of our belief in the ether. If light takes several years to reach us from a distant star, it is no longer on the star, nor is it on the earth. It must be somewhere, and supported, so to speak, by some material agency.

The same idea may be expressed in a more mathematical and more abstract form. What we note are the changes undergone by the material molecules. We see, for instance, that the photographic plate experiences the consequences of a phenomenon of which the incandescent mass of a star was the scene several years before. Now, in ordinary mechanics, the state of the system under consideration depends only on its state at the moment immediately preceding; the system therefore satisfies certain differential equations. On the other hand, if we did not believe in the ether, the state of the material universe would depend not only on the state immediately preceding, but also on much older states; the system would satisfy equations of finite differences. The ether was invented to escape this breaking down of the laws of general mechanics.

Still, this would only compel us to fill the interplanetary space with ether, but not to make it penetrate into the midst of the material media. Fizeau's experiment goes further. By the interference of rays which have passed through the air or water in motion, it seems to show us two different media penetrating each other, and yet being displaced with respect to each other. The ether is all but in our grasp. Experiments can be conceived in which we come closer still to it. Assume that Newton's principle of the equality of action and re-action is not true if applied to matter *alone*, and that this can be proved. The geometrical sum of all the forces applied to all the molecules would no longer be zero. If we did not wish to change the whole of the science of mechanics, we should have to introduce the ether, in order that the action which matter apparently undergoes should be counterbalanced by the re-action of matter on something.

Or again, suppose we discover that optical and electrical phenomena are influenced by the motion of the earth. It would follow that those phenomena might reveal to us not only the relative motion of material bodies, but also what would seem to be their absolute motion. Again, it would be necessary to have an ether in order that these so-called absolute movements should not be their displacements with respect to empty space, but with respect to something concrete.

Will this ever be accomplished? I do not think so, and I shall explain why; and yet, it is not absurd, for others have entertained this view. For instance, if the theory of Lorentz, of which I shall speak in more detail in Chapter XIII., were true, Newton's principle would not apply to matter *alone*, and the difference would not be very far from being within reach of experiment. On the other hand, many experiments have been made on the influence of the motion of the earth. The results have always been negative. But if these experiments have been undertaken, it is because we have not been certain beforehand; and indeed, according to current theories, the compensation would be only approximate, and we might expect to find accurate methods giving positive results. I think that such a hope is illusory; it was none the less interesting to show that a success of this kind would, in a certain sense, open to us a new world.

And now allow me to make a digression; I

must explain why I do not believe, in spite of Lorentz, that more exact observations will ever make evident anything else but the relative displacements of material bodies. Experiments have been made that should have disclosed the terms of the first order; the results were nugatory. Could that have been by chance? No one has admitted this; a general explanation was sought, and Lorentz found it. He showed that the terms of the first order should cancel each other, but not the terms of the second order. Then more exact experiments were made, which were also negative; neither could this be the result of chance. An explanation was necessary, and was forthcoming; they always are; hypotheses are what we lack the least. But this is not enough. Who is there who does not think that this leaves to chance far too important a rôle? Would it not also be a chance that this singular concurrence should cause a certain circumstance to destroy the terms of the first order, and that a totally different but very opportune circumstance should cause those of the second order to vanish? No; the same explanation must be found for the two cases, and everything tends to show that this explanation would serve equally well for the terms of the higher order, and that the mutual destruction of these terms will be rigorous and absolute.

*The Present State of Physics.*—Two opposite tendencies may be distinguished in the history of the development of physics. On the one hand, new relations are continually being discovered between objects which seemed destined to remain for ever unconnected; scattered facts cease to be strangers to each other and tend to be marshalled into an imposing synthesis. The march of science is towards unity and simplicity.

On the other hand, new phenomena are continually being revealed; it will be long before they can be assigned their place—sometimes it may happen that to find them a place a corner of the edifice must be demolished. In the same way, we are continually perceiving details ever more varied in the phenomena we know, where our crude senses used to be unable to detect any lack of unity. What we thought to be simple becomes complex, and the march of science seems to be towards diversity and complication.

Here, then, are two opposing tendencies, each of which seems to triumph in turn. Which will win? If the first wins, science is possible; but nothing proves this *à priori*, and it may be that after unsuccessful efforts to bend Nature to our ideal of unity in spite of herself, we shall be submerged by the ever-rising flood of our new riches and compelled to renounce all idea of classification—to abandon our ideal, and to reduce science to the mere recording of innumerable recipes.

In fact, we can give this question no answer. All that we can do is to observe the science of to-day, and compare it with that of yesterday.

No doubt after this examination we shall be in a position to offer a few conjectures.

Half-a-century ago hopes ran high indeed. The unity of force had just been revealed to us by the discovery of the conservation of energy and of its transformation. This discovery also showed that the phenomena of heat could be explained by molecular movements. Although the nature of these movements was not exactly known, no one doubted but that they would be ascertained before long. As for light, the work seemed entirely completed. So far as electricity was concerned, there was not so great an advance. Electricity had just annexed magnetism. This was a considerable and a definitive step towards unity. But how was electricity in its turn to be brought into the general unity, and how was it to be included in the general universal mechanism? No one had the slightest idea. As to the possibility of the inclusion, all were agreed; they had faith. Finally, as far as the molecular properties of material bodies are concerned, the inclusion seemed easier, but the details were very hazy. In a word, hopes were vast and strong, but vague.

To-day, what do we see? In the first place, a step in advance—immense progress. The relations between light and electricity are now known; the three domains of light, electricity, and magnetism, formerly separated, are now one; and this annexation seems definitive.

Nevertheless the conquest has caused us some

sacrifices. Optical phenomena become particular cases in electric phenomena; as long as the former remained isolated, it was easy to explain them by movements which were thought to be known in all their details. That was easy enough; but any explanation to be accepted must now cover the whole domain of electricity. This cannot be done without difficulty.

The most satisfactory theory is that of Lorentz; it is unquestionably the theory that best explains the known facts, the one that throws into relief the greatest number of known relations, the one in which we find most traces of definitive construction. That it still possesses a serious fault I have shown above. It is in contradiction with Newton's law that action and re-action are equal and opposite—or rather, this principle according to Lorentz cannot be applicable to matter alone; if it be true, it must take into account the action of the ether on matter, and the re-action of the matter on the ether. Now, in the new order, it is very likely that things do not happen in this way.

However this may be, it is due to Lorentz that the results of Fizeau on the optics of moving bodies, the laws of normal and abnormal dispersion and of absorption are connected with each other and with the other properties of the ether, by bonds which no doubt will not be readily severed. Look at the ease with which the new Zeeman phenomenon found its place, and even aided the classification of Faraday's magnetic rotation, which had defied all Maxwell's efforts. This facility proves that Lorentz's theory is not a mere artificial combination which must eventually find its solvent. It will probably have to be modified, but not destroyed.

The only object of Lorentz was to include in a single whole all the optics and electro-dynamics of moving bodies; he did not claim to give a mechanical explanation. Larmor goes further; keeping the essential part of Lorentz's theory, he grafts upon it, so to speak, MacCullagh's ideas on the direction of the movement of the ether. MacCullagh held that the velocity of the ether is the same in magnitude and direction as the magnetic force. Ingenious as is this attempt, the fault in Lorentz's theory remains, and is even aggravated. According to Lorentz, we do not know what the movements of the ether are; and because we do not know this, we may suppose them to be movements compensating those of matter, and re-affirming that action and re-action are equal and opposite. According to Larmor we know the movements of the ether, and we can prove that the compensation does not take place.

If Larmor has failed, as in my opinion he has, does it necessarily follow that a mechanical explanation is impossible? Far from it. I said above that as long as a phenomenon obeys the two principles of energy and least action, so long it allows of an unlimited number of mechanical explanations. And so with the phenomena of optics and electricity.

But this is not enough. For a mechanical explanation to be good it must be simple; to choose it from among all the explanations that are possible there must be other reasons than the necessity of making a choice. Well, we have no theory as yet which will satisfy this condition and consequently be of any use. Are we then to complain? That would be to forget the end we seek, which is not the mechanism; the true and only aim is unity.

We ought therefore to set some limits to our ambition. Let us not seek to formulate a mechanical explanation; let us be content to show that we can always find one if we wish. In this we have succeeded. The principle of the conservation of energy has always been confirmed, and now it has a fellow in the principle of least action, stated in the form appropriate to physics. This has also been verified, at least as far as concerns the reversible phenomena which obey Lagrange's equations—in other words, which obey the most general laws of physics. The irreversible phenomena are much more difficult to bring into line; but they, too, are being co-ordinated and tend to come into the unity. The light which illuminates them comes from Carnot's principle. For a long time thermo-dynamics was confined to the study of the dilatations of bodies and of their change of state. For some time past it has been growing bolder, and has considerably extended its domain. We owe to it the theories of the voltaic cell and of their thermo-electric phenomena; there is not a corner in physics which it has not explored, and it has even attacked chemistry itself. The same laws hold good; everywhere, disguised in some form or other, we find Carnot's principle; everywhere also appears that eminently abstract concept of entropy which is as universal as the concept of energy, and like it, seems to conceal a reality. It seemed that radiant heat must escape, but recently that, too, has been brought under the same laws.

In this way fresh analogies are revealed which may be often pursued in detail; electric resistance resembles the viscosity of fluids; hysteresis would rather be like the friction of solids. In all cases friction appears to be the type most imitated by the most diverse irreversible phenomena, and this relationship is real and profound.

A strictly mechanical explanation of these phenomena has also been sought, but, owing to their nature, it is hardly likely that it will be found. To find it, it has been necessary to suppose that the irreversibility is but apparent, that the elementary phenomena are reversible and obey the known laws of dynamics. But the elements are extremely numerous, and become blended more and more, so that to our crude sight all appears to tend towards uniformity—*i.e.*, all seems to progress in the same direction, and that without hope of return. The apparent irreversibility is therefore but an effect of the law of great numbers. Only a being of infinitely subtle senses, such as Maxwell's demon, could unravel this tangled skein and turn back the course of the universe.

This conception, which is connected with the kinetic theory of gases, has cost great effort and has not, on the whole, been fruitful; it may become so. This is not the place to examine if it leads to contradictions, and if it is in conformity with the true nature of things.

Let us notice, however, the original ideas of M. Gouy on the Brownian movement. According to this scientist, this singular movement does not obey Carnot's principle. The particles which it sets moving would be smaller than the meshes of that tightly drawn net; they would thus be ready to separate them, and thereby to set back the course of the universe. One can almost see Maxwell's demon at work.[1]

To resume, phenomena long known are gradually being better classified, but new phenomena come to claim their place, and most of them, like the Zeeman effect, find it at once. Then we have the cathode rays, the X-rays, uranium and radium rays; in fact, a whole world of which none had suspected the existence. How many unexpected

[1] Clerk-Maxwell imagined some supernatural agency at work, sorting molecules in a gas of uniform temperature into (a) those possessing kinetic energy above the average, (b) those possessing kinetic energy below the average.—[TR.]

guests to find a place for! No one can yet predict the place they will occupy, but I do not believe they will destroy the general unity; I think that they will rather complete it. On the one hand, indeed, the new radiations seem to be connected with the phenomena of luminosity; not only do they excite fluorescence, but they sometimes come into existence under the same conditions as that property; neither are they unrelated to the cause which produces the electric spark under the action of ultra-violet light. Finally, and most important of all, it is believed that in all these phenomena there exist ions, animated, it is true, with velocities far greater than those of electrolytes. All this is very vague, but it will all become clearer.

Phosphorescence and the action of light on the spark were regions rather isolated, and consequently somewhat neglected by investigators. It is to be hoped that a new path will now be made which will facilitate their communications with the rest of science. Not only do we discover new phenomena, but those we think we know are revealed in unlooked-for aspects. In the free ether the laws preserve their majestic simplicity, but matter properly so called seems more and more complex; all we can say of it is but approximate, and our formulæ are constantly requiring new terms.

But the ranks are unbroken, the relations that we have discovered between objects we thought simple still hold good between the same objects when their complexity is recognised, and that alone is the important thing. Our equations become, it is true, more and more complicated, so as to embrace more closely the complexity of nature; but nothing is changed in the relations which enable these equations to be derived from each other. In a word, the form of these equations persists. Take for instance the laws of reflection. Fresnel established them by a simple and attractive theory which experiment seemed to confirm. Subsequently, more accurate researches have shown that this verification was but approximate; traces of elliptic polarisation were detected everywhere. But it is owing to the first approximation that the cause of these anomalies was found in the existence of a transition layer, and all the essentials of Fresnel's theory have remained. We cannot help reflecting that all these relations would never have been noted if there had been doubt in the first place as to the complexity of the objects they connect. Long ago it was said: If Tycho had had instruments ten times as precise, we would never have had a Kepler, or a Newton, or Astronomy. It is a misfortune for a science to be born too late, when the means of observation have become too perfect. That is what is happening at this moment with respect to physical chemistry; the founders are hampered in their general grasp by third and fourth decimal places; happily they are men of robust faith. As we get to know the properties of matter better we see that continuity reigns.

From the work of Andrews and Van der Waals, we see how the transition from the liquid to the gaseous state is made, and that it is not abrupt. Similarly, there is no gap between the liquid and solid states, and in the proceedings of a recent Congress we see memoirs on the rigidity of liquids side by side with papers on the flow of solids.

With this tendency there is no doubt a loss of simplicity. Such and such an effect was represented by straight lines; it is now necessary to connect these lines by more or less complicated curves. On the other hand, unity is gained. Separate categories quieted but did not satisfy the mind.

Finally, a new domain, that of chemistry, has been invaded by the method of physics, and we see the birth of physical chemistry. It is still quite young, but already it has enabled us to connect such phenomena as electrolysis, osmosis, and the movements of ions.

From this cursory exposition what can we conclude? Taking all things into account, we have approached the realisation of unity. This has not been done as quickly as was hoped fifty years ago, and the path predicted has not always been followed; but, on the whole, much ground has been gained.

# CHAPTER XI.

No doubt the reader will be astonished to find reflections on the calculus of probabilities in such a volume as this. What has that calculus to do with physical science? The questions I shall raise —without, however, giving them a solution—are naturally raised by the philosopher who is examining the problems of physics. So far is this the case, that in the two preceding chapters I have several times used the words "probability" and "chance." "Predicted facts," as I said above, "can only be probable." However solidly founded a prediction may appear to be, we are never absolutely certain that experiment will not prove it false; but the probability is often so great that practically it may be accepted. And a little farther on I added:—"See what a part the belief in simplicity plays in our generalisations. We have verified a simple law in a large number of particular cases, and we refuse to admit that this so-often-repeated coincidence is a mere effect of chance." Thus, in a multitude of circumstances the physicist is often in the same position as the gambler who reckons up his chances. Every time that he reasons by

induction, he more or less consciously requires the
calculus of probabilities, and that is why I am
obliged to open this chapter parenthetically, and to
interrupt our discussion of method in the physical
sciences in order to examine a little closer what this
calculus is worth, and what dependençe we may
place upon it.    The very name of the calculus of
probabilities is a paradox.    Probability as opposed
to certainty is what one does not know, and how
can we calculate the unknown?    Yet many eminent
scientists have devoted themselves to this calculus,
and it cannot be denied that science has drawn there-
from no small advantage.    How can we explain
this apparent contradiction?    Has probability been
defined?    Can it even be defined?    And if it cannot, how can we venture to reason upon it?    The
definition, it will be said, is very simple.    The
probability of an event is the ratio of the number
of cases favourable to the event to the total number
of possible cases.    A simple example will show how
incomplete this definition is:—I throw two dice.
What is the probability that one of the two
at least turns up a 6?    Each can turn up in six
different ways;  the number of possible cases is
$6 \times 6 = 36$.    The number of favourable cases is 11;
the probability is $\frac{11}{36}$.    That is the correct solution.
But why cannot we just as well proceed as follows?
—The points which turn up on the two dice form
$\frac{6 \times 7}{2} = 21$ different combinations.    Among these
combinations, six are favourable;  the probability

is $\frac{6}{21}$. Now why is the first method of calculating the number of possible cases more legitimate than the second? In any case it is not the definition that tells us. We are therefore bound to complete the definition by saying, ". . . to the total number of possible cases, provided the cases are equally probable." So we are compelled to define the probable by the probable. How can we know that two possible cases are equally probable? Will it be by a convention? If we insert at the beginning of every problem an explicit convention, well and good! We then have nothing to do but to apply the rules of arithmetic and algebra, and we complete our calculation, when our result cannot be called in question. But if we wish to make the slightest application of this result, we must prove that our convention is legitimate, and we shall find ourselves in the presence of the very difficulty we thought we had avoided. It may be said that common-sense is enough to show us the convention that should be adopted. Alas! M. Bertrand has amused himself by discussing the following simple problem:—"What is the probability that a chord of a circle may be greater than the side of the inscribed equilateral triangle?" The illustrious geometer successively adopted two conventions which seemed to be equally imperative in the eyes of common-sense, and with one convention he finds $\frac{1}{2}$, and with the other $\frac{1}{3}$. The conclusion which seems to follow from this is that the calculus of probabilities is a useless science, that the obscure

instinct which we call common-sense, and to which
we appeal for the legitimisation of our conventions,
must be distrusted.    But to this conclusion we can
no longer subscribe.    We cannot do without that
obscure instinct.    Without it, science would be
impossible, and without it we could neither discover
nor apply a law.    Have we any right, for instance,
to enunciate Newton's law?    No doubt numerous
observations are in agreement with it, but is not
that a simple fact of chance?    and how do we know,
besides, that this law which has been true for so
many generations will not be untrue in the next?
To this objection the only answer you can give is:
It is very improbable.    But grant the law.    By
means of it I can calculate the position of Jupiter
in a year from now.    Yet have I any right to say
this?    Who can tell if a gigantic mass of enormous
velocity is not going to pass near the solar system
and produce unforeseen perturbations?    Here
again the only answer is:  It is very improbable.
From this point of view all the sciences would only
be unconscious applications of the calculus of probabilities.    And if this calculus be condemned, then
the whole of the sciences must also be condemned.
I shall not dwell at length on scientific problems
in which the intervention of the calculus of probabilities is more evident.    In the forefront of these
is the problem of interpolation, in which, knowing
a certain number of values of a function, we try
to discover the intermediary values.    I may also
mention the celebrated theory of errors of observa-

tion, to which I shall return later; the kinetic theory of gases, a well-known hypothesis wherein each gaseous molecule is supposed to describe an extremely complicated path, but in which, through the effect of great numbers, the mean phenomena which are all we observe obey the simple laws of Mariotte and Gay-Lussac. All these theories are based upon the laws of great numbers, and the calculus of probabilities would evidently involve them in its ruin. It is true that they have only a particular interest, and that, save as far as inter-polation is concerned, they are sacrifices to which we might readily be resigned. But I have said above, it would not be these partial sacrifices that would be in question; it would be the legitimacy of the whole of science that would be challenged. I quite see that it might be said: We do not know, and yet we must act. As for action, we have not time to devote ourselves to an inquiry that will suffice to dispel our ignorance. Besides, such an inquiry would demand unlimited time. We must therefore make up our minds without knowing. This must be often done whatever may happen, and we must follow the rules although we may have but little confidence in them. What I know is, not that such a thing is true, but that the best course for me is to act as if it were true. The calculus of probabilities, and therefore science itself, would be no longer of any practical value.

Unfortunately the difficulty does not thus dis-appear. A gambler wants to try a *coup*, and he asks my advice. If I give it him, I use the calculus of probabilities; but I shall not guarantee success. That is what I shall call *subjective probability*. In this case we might be content with the explanation of which I have just given a sketch. But assume that an observer is present at the play, that he knows of the *coup*, and that play goes on for a long time, and that he makes a summary of his notes. He will find that events have taken place in conformity with the laws of the calculus of probabilities. That is what I shall call *objective probability*, and it is this phenomenon which has to be explained. There are numerous Insurance Societies which apply the rules of the calculus of probabilities, and they distribute to their shareholders dividends, the objective reality of which cannot be contested. In order to explain them, we must do more than invoke our ignorance and the necessity of action. Thus, absolute scepticism is not admissible. We may distrust, but we cannot condemn *en bloc*. Discussion is necessary.

I. *Classification of the Problems of Probability.*—In order to classify the problems which are presented to us with reference to probabilities, we must look at them from different points of view, and first of all, from that of *generality*. I said above that probability is the ratio of the number of favourable to the number of possible cases. What for want of a better term I call generality will increase with the number of possible cases. This number may be finite, as, for instance, if we take a throw of the dice in which the number of possible cases is 36. That is the first degree of generality. But if we ask, for instance, what is the probability that a point within a circle is within the inscribed square, there are as many possible cases as there are points in the circle—that is to say, an infinite number. This is the second degree of generality. Generality can be pushed further still. We may ask the probability that a function will satisfy a given condition. There are then as many possible cases as one can imagine different functions. This is the third degree of generality, which we reach, for instance, when we try to find the most probable law after a finite number of observations. Yet we may place ourselves at a quite different point of view. If we were not ignorant there would be no probability, there could only be certainty. But our ignorance cannot be absolute, for then there would be no longer any probability at all. Thus the problems of probability may be classed according to the greater or less depth of this ignorance. In mathematics we may set ourselves problems in probability. What is the probability that the fifth decimal of a logarithm taken at random from a table is a 9. There is no hesitation in answering that this probability is 1-10th. Here we possess all the data of the problem. We can calculate our logarithm without having recourse to the table, but we need not give ourselves the trouble. This is the first degree of ignorance. In the physical sciences our ignorance is already greater.

The state of a system at a given moment depends
on two things—its initial state, and the law
according to which that state varies. If we know
both this law and this initial state, we have a
simple mathematical problem to solve, and we
fall back upon our first degree of ignorance.
Then it often happens that we know the law
and do not know the initial state. It may be
asked, for instance, what is the present distribution of the minor planets? We know that from
all time they have obeyed the laws of Kepler,
but we do not know what was their initial distribution. In the kinetic theory of gases we
assume that the gaseous molecules follow rectilinear paths and obey the laws of impact and
elastic bodies; yet as we know nothing of their
initial velocities, we know nothing of their present
velocities. The calculus of probabilities alone
enables us to predict the mean phenomena which
will result from a combination of these velocities.
This is the second degree of ignorance. Finally
it is possible, that not only the initial conditions
but the laws themselves are unknown. We then
reach the third degree of ignorance, and in general
we can no longer affirm anything at all as to the
probability of a phenomenon. It often happens
that instead of trying to discover an event by
means of a more or less imperfect knowledge of
the law, the events may be known, and we want
to find the law; or that, instead of deducing
effects from causes, we wish to deduce the causes

from the effects. Now, these problems are classified as *probability of causes*, and are the most interesting of all from their scientific applications. I play at *écarté* with a gentleman whom I know to be perfectly honest. What is the chance that he turns up the king? It is $\frac{1}{8}$. This is a problem of the probability of effects. I play with a gentleman whom I do not know. He has dealt ten times, and he has turned the king up six times. What is the chance that he is a sharper? This is a problem in the probability of causes. It may be said that it is the essential problem of the experimental method. I have observed $n$ values of $x$ and the corresponding values of $y$. I have found that the ratio of the latter to the former is practically constant. There is the event; what is the cause? Is it probable that there is a general law according to which $y$ would be proportional to $x$, and that small divergencies are due to errors of observation? This is the type of question that we are ever asking, and which we unconsciously solve whenever we are engaged in scientific work. I am now going to pass in review these different categories of problems by discussing in succession what I have called subjective and objective probability.

II. *Probability in Mathematics.*—The impossibility of squaring the circle was shown in 1885, but before that date all geometers considered this impossibility as so "probable" that the Académie des Sciences rejected without examination the, alas!

too numerous memoirs on this subject that a
few unhappy madmen sent in every year. Was
the Académie wrong? Evidently not, and it
knew perfectly well that by acting in this
manner it did not run the least risk of stifling
a discovery of moment. The Académie could
not have proved that it was right, but it knew
quite well that its instinct did not deceive it.
If you had asked the Academicians, they would
have answered: "We have compared the probability that an unknown scientist should have
found out what has been vainly sought for so
long, with the probability that there is one mad-
man the more on the earth, and the latter has
appeared to us the greater." These are very
good reasons, but there is nothing mathematical
about them; they are purely psychological. If
you had pressed them further, they would have
added: "Why do you expect a particular value of
a transcendental function to be an algebraical
number; if $\pi$ be the root of an algebraical equation, why do you expect this root to be a period of
the function $sin\ 2x$, and why is it not the same
with the other roots of the same equation?" To
sum up, they would have invoked the principle of
sufficient reason in its vaguest form. Yet what
information could they draw from it? At most a
rule of conduct for the employment of their time,
which would be more usefully spent at their
ordinary work than in reading a lucubration
that inspired in them a legitimate distrust. But

what I called above objective probability has
nothing in common with this first problem.   It is
otherwise with the second.   Let us consider the
first 10,000 logarithms that we find in a table.
Among these 10,000 logarithms I take one at
random.   What is the probability that its third
decimal is an even number?   You will say with-
out any hesitation that the probability is $\frac{1}{2}$, and in
fact if you pick out in a table the third decimals
in these 10,000 numbers you will find nearly as
many even digits as odd.   Or, if you prefer it, let
us write 10,000 numbers corresponding to our
10,000 logarithms, writing down for each of these
numbers + 1 if the third decimal of the corresponding logarithm is even, and – 1 if odd; and then
let us take the mean of these 10,000 numbers.   I
do not hesitate to say that the mean of these
10,000 units is probably zero, and if I were to
calculate it practically, I would verify that it is
extremely small.   But this verification is needless.
I might have rigorously proved that this mean is
smaller than 0.003.   To prove this result I should
have had to make a rather long calculation for
which there is no room here, and for which I
may refer the reader to an article that I published in the *Revue générale des Sciences*, April
15th, 1899.   The only point to which I wish to
draw attention is the following.   In this calculation I had occasion to rest my case on only two
facts—namely, that the first and second derivatives
of the logarithm remain, in the interval considered,

between certain limits.  Hence our first conclusion is that the property is not only true of the logarithm but of any continuous function whatever, since the derivatives of every continuous function are limited.  If I was certain beforehand of the result, it is because I have often observed analogous facts for other continuous functions; and next, it is because I went through in my mind in a more or less unconscious and imperfect manner the reasoning which led me to the preceding inequalities, just as a skilled calculator before finishing his multiplication takes into account what it ought to come to approximately.  And besides, since what I call my intuition was only an incomplete summary of a piece of true reasoning, it is clear that observation has confirmed my predictions, and that the objective and subjective probabilities are in agreement.  As a third example I shall choose the following:—The number $u$ is taken at random and $n$ is a given very large integer.  What is the mean value of sin $nu$?  This problem has no meaning by itself.  To give it one, a convention is required—namely, we agree that the probability for the number $u$ to lie between $a$ and $a+da$ is $\phi(a)da$; that it is therefore proportional to the infinitely small interval $da$, and is equal to this multiplied by a function $\phi(a)$, only depending on $a$.  As for this function I choose it arbitrarily, but I must assume it to be continuous.  The value of sin $nu$ remaining the same when $u$ increases by $2\pi$, I may without loss of generality assume that

$u$ lies between o and $2\pi$, and I shall thus be led to suppose that $\phi(a)$ is a periodic function whose period is $2\pi$. The mean value that we seek is readily expressed by a simple integral, and it is easy to show that this integral is smaller than $\dfrac{2\pi M_K}{n^K}$, $M_K$ being the maximum value of the $K$th derivative of $\phi(u)$. We see then that if the $K$th derivative is finite, our mean value will tend towards zero when $n$ increases indefinitely, and that more rapidly than $\dfrac{1}{n^{K-1}}$. The mean value of sin $nu$ when $n$ is very large is therefore zero. To define this value I required a convention, but the result remains the same *whatever that convention may be*. I have imposed upon myself but slight restrictions when I assumed that the function $\phi(a)$ is continuous and periodic, and these hypotheses are so natural that we may ask ourselves how they can be escaped. Examination of the three preceding examples, so different in all respects, has already given us a glimpse on the one hand of the rôle of what philosophers call the principle of sufficient reason, and on the other hand of the importance of the fact that certain properties are common to all continuous functions. The study of probability in the physical sciences will lead us to the same result.

III. *Probability in the Physical Sciences.*—We now come to the problems which are connected with what I have called the second degree of ignorance—namely, those in which we know the law but do not know the initial state of the system. I could multiply examples, but I shall take only one. What is the probable present distribution of the minor planets on the zodiac? We know they obey the laws of Kepler. We may even, without changing the nature of the problem, suppose that their orbits are circular and situated in the same plane, a plane which we are given. On the other hand, we know absolutely nothing about their initial distribution. However, we do not hesitate to affirm that this distribution is now nearly uniform. Why? Let $b$ be the longitude of a minor planet in the initial epoch—that is to say, the epoch zero. Let $a$ be its mean motion. Its longitude at the present time—i.e., at the time $t$ will be $at + b$. To say that the present distribution is uniform is to say that the mean value of the sines and cosines of multiples of $at + b$ is zero. Why do we assert this? Let us represent our minor planet by a point in a plane—namely, the point whose co-ordinates are $a$ and $b$. All these representative points will be contained in a certain region of the plane, but as they are very numerous this region will appear dotted with points. We know nothing else about the distribution of the points. Now what do we do when we apply the calculus of probabilities to such a question as this? What is the probability that one or more representative points may be found in a certain portion of the plane? In our ignorance we are compelled to make an arbitrary hypothesis. To explain the nature of this hypothesis I may be allowed to use, instead of a mathematical formula, a crude but concrete image. Let us suppose that over the surface of our plane has been spread imaginary matter, the density of which is variable, but varies continuously. We shall then agree to say that the probable number of representative points to be found on a certain portion of the plane is proportional to the quantity of this imaginary matter which is found there. If there are, then, two regions of the plane of the same extent, the probabilities that a representative point of one of our minor planets is in one or other of these regions will be as the mean densities of the imaginary matter in one or other of the regions. Here then are two distributions, one real, in which the representative points are very numerous, very close together, but discrete like the molecules of matter in the atomic hypothesis; the other remote from reality, in which our representative points are replaced by imaginary continuous matter. We know that the latter cannot be real, but we are forced to adopt it through our ignorance. If, again, we had some idea of the real distribution of the representative points, we could arrange it so that in a region of some extent the density of this imaginary continuous matter may be nearly proportional to the number of representative points, or, if it is preferred, to the number of atoms which are contained in that region. Even that is impossible, and our ignorance is so great that we are forced to choose arbitrarily the function which defines the density of our imaginary matter. We shall be compelled to adopt a hypothesis from which we can hardly get away; we shall suppose that this function is continuous. That is sufficient, as we shall see, to enable us to reach our conclusion.

What is at the instant $t$ the probable distribution of the minor planets—or rather, what is the mean value of the sine of the longitude at the moment $t$—i.e., of sin $(at + b)$? We made at the outset an arbitrary convention, but if we adopt it, this probable value is entirely defined. Let us decompose the plane into elements of surface. Consider the value of sin $(at + b)$ at the centre of each of these elements. Multiply this value by the surface of the element and by the corresponding density of the imaginary matter. Let us then take the sum for all the elements of the plane. This sum, by definition, will be the probable mean value we seek, which will thus be expressed by a double integral. It may be thought at first that this mean value depends on the choice of the function $\phi$ which defines the density of the imaginary matter, and as this function $\phi$ is arbitrary, we can, according to the arbitrary choice which we make, obtain a certain mean value. But this is not the case. A simple calculation shows us that our double integral decreases very rapidly as $t$ increases. Thus, I cannot tell what hypothesis to make as to the probability of this or that initial distribution, but when once the hypothesis is made the result will be the same, and this gets me out of my difficulty. Whatever the function $\phi$ may be, the mean value tends towards zero as $t$ increases, and as the minor planets have certainly accomplished a very large number of revolutions, I may assert that this mean value is very small. I may give to $\phi$ any value I choose, with one restriction: this function must be continuous; and, in fact, from the point of view of subjective probability, the choice of a discontinuous function would have been unreasonable. What reason could I have, for instance, for supposing that the initial longitude might be exactly $o°$, but that it could not lie between $o°$ and $1°$?

The difficulty reappears if we look at it from the point of view of objective probability; if we pass from our imaginary distribution in which the supposititious matter was assumed to be continuous, to the real distribution in which our representative points are formed as discrete atoms. The mean value of sin $(at+b)$ will be represented quite simply by

$$\frac{1}{n} \; \Sigma \; \sin \, (at + b),$$

$n$ being the number of minor planets. Instead of a double integral referring to a continuous function, we shall have a sum of discrete terms. However, no one will seriously doubt that this mean value is practically very small. Our representative points being very close together, our discrete sum will in general differ very little from an integral. An integral is the limit towards which a sum of terms tends when the number of these terms is indefinitely increased. If the terms are very numerous, the sum will differ very little from its limit—that is to say, from the integral, and what I said of the latter will still be true of the sum itself. But there are exceptions. If, for instance, for all the minor planets $b = \frac{\pi}{2} - at$, the longitude of all the planets at the time $t$ would be $\frac{\pi}{2}$, and the mean value in question would be evidently unity. For this to be the case at the time $o$, the minor planets must have all been lying on a kind of spiral of peculiar form, with its spires very close together. All will admit that such an initial distribution is extremely improbable (and even if it were realised, the distribution would not be uniform at the present time—for example, on the 1st January 1900; but it would become so a few years later). Why, then, do we think this initial distribution improbable? This must be explained, for if we are wrong in rejecting as improbable this absurd hypothesis, our inquiry breaks down, and we can no longer affirm anything on the subject of the probability of this or that present distribution. Once more we shall invoke the principle of sufficient reason, to which we must always recur. We might admit that at the beginning the planets were distributed almost in a straight line.  We might admit that they were irregularly distributed.  But it seems to us that there is no sufficient reason for the unknown cause that gave them birth to have acted along a curve so regular and yet so complicated, which would appear to have been expressly chosen so that the distribution at the present day would not be uniform.

IV. *Rouge et Noir.*—The questions raised by games of chance, such as roulette, are, fundamentally, quite analogous to those we have just treated.  For example, a wheel is divided into thirty-seven equal compartments, alternately red and black.  A ball is spun round the wheel, and after having moved round a number of times, it stops in front of one of these sub-divisions.  The probability that the division is red is obviously $\frac{1}{2}$.  The needle describes an angle $\theta$, including several complete revolutions.  I do not know what is the probability that the ball is spun with such a force that this angle should lie between $\theta$ and $\theta + d\theta$, but I can make a convention.  I can suppose that this probability is $\phi(\theta)d\theta$.  As for the function $\phi(\theta)$, I can choose it in an entirely arbitrary manner.  I have nothing to guide me in my choice, but I am naturally induced to suppose the function to be continuous.  Let $\epsilon$ be a length (measured on the circumference of the circle of radius unity) of each red and black compartment.  We have to calculate the integral of $\phi(\theta)d\theta$, extending it on the one hand to all the red, and on the other hand to all the black compartments, and to compare the results. Consider an interval 2 $\epsilon$ comprising two consecutive red and black compartments. Let M and $m$ be the maximum and minimum values of the function $\phi(\theta)$ in this interval. The integral extended to the red compartments will be smaller than $\Sigma$ M$\epsilon$; extended to the black it will be greater than $\Sigma$ $m\epsilon$. The difference will therefore be smaller than $\Sigma$ (M – $m$) $\epsilon$. But if the function $\phi$ is supposed continuous, and if on the other hand the interval $\epsilon$ is very small with respect to the total angle described by the needle, the difference M – $m$ will be very small. The difference of the two integrals will be therefore very small, and the probability will be very nearly $\frac{1}{2}$. We see that without knowing anything of the function $\phi$ we must act as if the probability were $\frac{1}{2}$. And on the other hand it explains why, from the objective point of view, if I watch a certain number of *coups*, observation will give me almost as many black *coups* as red. All the players know this objective law; but it leads them into a remarkable error, which has often been exposed, but into which they are always falling. When the red has won, for example, six times running, they bet on black, thinking that they are playing an absolutely safe game, because they say it is a very rare thing for the red to win seven times running. In reality their probability of winning is still $\frac{1}{2}$. Observation shows, it is true, that the series of seven consecutive reds is very rare, but series of six reds followed by a black are also very rare. They have noticed the rarity of the series of seven reds; if they have not remarked the rarity of six reds and a black, it is only because such series strike the attention less.

V. *The Probability of Causes.*—We now come to the problems of the probability of causes, the most important from the point of view of scientific applications. Two stars, for instance, are very close together on the celestial sphere. Is this apparent contiguity a mere effect of chance? Are these stars, although almost on the same visual ray, situated at very different distances from the earth, and therefore very far indeed from one another? or does the apparent correspond to a real contiguity? This is a problem on the probability of causes.

First of all, I recall that at the outset of all problems of probability of effects that have occupied our attention up to now, we have had to use a convention which was more or less justified; and if in most cases the result was to a certain extent independent of this convention, it was only the condition of certain hypotheses which enabled us *à priori* to reject discontinuous functions, for example, or certain absurd conventions. We shall again find something analogous to this when we deal with the probability of causes. An effect may be produced by the cause $a$ or by the cause $b$. The effect has just been observed. We ask the probability that it is due to the cause *a*. This is an *à posteriori* probability of cause. But I could not calculate it, if a convention more or less justified did not tell me in advance what is the *à priori* probability for the cause *a* to come into play— I mean the probability of this event to some one who had not observed the effect. To make my meaning clearer, I go back to the game of *écarté* mentioned before. My adversary deals for the first time and turns up a king. What is the probability that he is a sharper? The formulæ ordinarily taught give $\frac{8}{9}$, a result which is obviously rather surprising. If we look at it closer, we see that the conclusion is arrived at as if, before sitting down at the table, I had considered that there was one chance in two that my adversary was not honest. An absurd hypothesis, because in that case I should certainly not have played with him; and this explains the absurdity of the conclusion. The function on the *à priori* probability was unjustified, and that is why the conclusion of the *à posteriori* probability led me into an inadmissible result. The importance of this preliminary convention is obvious. I shall even add that if none were made, the problem of the *à posteriori* probability would have no meaning. It must be always made either explicitly or tacitly.

Let us pass on to an example of a more scientific character. I require to determine an experimental law; this law, when discovered, can be represented by a curve. I make a certain number of isolated observations, each of which may be represented by a point. When I have obtained these different points, I draw a curve between them as carefully as possible, giving my curve a regular form, avoiding sharp angles, accentuated inflexions, and any sudden variation of the radius of curvature. This curve will represent to me the probable law, and not only will it give me the values of the functions intermediary to those which have been observed, but it also gives me the observed values more accurately than direct observation does; that is why I make the curve pass near the points and not through the points themselves.

Here, then, is a problem in the probability of causes. The effects are the measurements I have recorded; they depend on the combination of two causes—the true law of the phenomenon and errors of observation. Knowing the effects, we have to find the probability that the phenomenon shall obey this law or that, and that the observations have been accompanied by this or that error. The most probable law, therefore, corresponds to the curve we have traced, and the most probable error is represented by the distance of the corresponding point from that curve. But the problem has no meaning if before the observations I had an *à priori* idea of the probability of this law or that, or of the chances of error to which I am exposed. If my instruments are good (and I knew whether this is so or not before beginning the observations), I shall not draw the curve far from the points which represent the rough measurements. If they are inferior, I may draw it a little farther from the points, so that I may get a less sinuous curve; much will be sacrificed to regularity.

Why, then, do I draw a curve without sinuosities? Because I consider *à priori* a law represented by a continuous function (or function the derivatives of which to a high order are small), as more probable than a law not satisfying those conditions. But for this conviction the problem would have no meaning; interpolation would be impossible; no law could be deduced from a finite number of observations; science would cease to exist.

Fifty years ago physicists considered, other things being equal, a simple law as more probable than a complicated law. This principle was even invoked in favour of Mariotte's law as against that of Regnault. But this belief is now repudiated; and yet, how many times are we compelled to act as though we still held it! However that may be, what remains of this tendency is the belief in continuity, and as we have just seen, if the belief in continuity were to disappear, experimental science would become impossible.

VI. *The Theory of Errors.*—We are thus brought to consider the theory of errors which is directly connected with the problem of the probability of causes. Here again we find *effects*—to wit, a certain number of irreconcilable observations, and we try to find the *causes* which are, on the one hand, the true value of the quantity to be measured, and, on the other, the error made in each isolated observation. We must calculate the probable *à posteriori* value of each error, and therefore the probable value of the quantity to be measured. But, as I have just explained, we cannot undertake this calculation unless we admit *à priori*—*i.e.*, before any observations are made— that there is a law of the probability of errors. Is there a law of errors? The law to which all calculators assent is Gauss's law, that is represented by a certain transcendental curve known as the "bell."

But it is first of all necessary to recall the classic distinction between systematic and accidental errors. If the metre with which we measure a length is too long, the number we get will be too small, and it will be no use to measure several times—that is a systematic error. If we measure with an accurate metre, we may make a mistake, and find the length sometimes too large and sometimes too small, and when we take the mean of a large number of measurements, the error will tend to grow small. These are accidental errors.

It is clear that systematic errors do not satisfy Gauss's law, but do accidental errors satisfy it?

Numerous proofs have been attempted, almost all of them crude paralogisms. But starting from the following hypotheses we may prove Gauss's law: the error is the result of a very large number of partial and independent errors; each partial error is very small and obeys any law of probability whatever, provided the probability of a positive error is the same as that of an equal negative error. It is clear that these conditions will be often, but not always, fulfilled, and we may reserve the name of accidental for errors which satisfy them.

We see that the method of least squares is not legitimate in every case; in general, physicists are more distrustful of it than astronomers. This is no doubt because the latter, apart from the systematic errors to which they and the physicists are subject alike, have to contend with an extremely important source of error which is entirely accidental—I mean atmospheric undulations. So it is very curious to hear a discussion between a physicist and an astronomer about a method of observation. The physicist, persuaded that one good measurement is worth more than many bad ones, is pre-eminently concerned with the elimination by means of every precaution of the final systematic errors; the astronomer retorts: "But you can only observe a small number of stars, and accidental errors will not disappear."

What conclusion must we draw? Must we continue to use the method of least squares?

We must distinguish. We have eliminated all the systematic errors of which we have any suspicion; we are quite certain that there are others still, but we cannot detect them; and yet we must make up our minds and adopt a definitive value which will be regarded as the probable value; and for that purpose it is clear that the best thing we can do is to apply Gauss's law. We have only applied a practical rule referring to subjective probability. And there is no more to be said.

Yet we want to go farther and say that not only the probable value is so much, but that the probable error in the result is so much. *This is absolutely invalid :* it would be true only if we were sure that all the systematic errors were eliminated, and of that we know absolutely nothing. We have two series of observations; by applying the law of least squares we find that the probable error in the first series is twice as small as in the second. The second series may, however, be more accurate than the first, because the first is perhaps affected by a large systematic error. All that we can say is, that the first series is *probably* better than the second because its accidental error is smaller, and that we have no reason for affirming that the systematic error is greater for one of the series than for the other, our ignorance on this point being absolute.

VII. *Conclusions.*—In the preceding lines I have set several problems, and have given no solution.

I do not regret this, for perhaps they will invite the reader to reflect on these delicate questions.

However that may be, there are certain points which seem to be well established. To undertake the calculation of any probability, and even for that calculation to have any meaning at all, we must admit, as a point of departure, an hypothesis or convention which has always something arbitrary about it. In the choice of this convention we can be guided only by the principle of sufficient reason. Unfortunately, this principle is very vague and very elastic, and in the cursory examination we have just made we have seen it assume different forms. The form under which we meet it most often is the belief in continuity, a belief which it would be difficult to justify by apodeictic reasoning, but without which all science would be impossible. Finally, the problems to which the calculus of probabilities may be applied with profit are those in which the result is independent of the hypothesis made at the outset, provided only that this hypothesis satisfies the condition of continuity.

# CHAPTER XII.[1]

## OPTICS AND ELECTRICITY.

*Fresnel's Theory.*—The best example that can be chosen is the theory of light and its relations to the theory of electricity. It is owing to Fresnel that the science of optics is more advanced than any other branch of physics. The theory called the theory of undulations forms a complete whole, which is satisfying to the mind; but we must not ask from it what it cannot give us. The object of mathematical theories is not to reveal to us the real nature of things; that would be an unreasonable claim. Their only object is to co-ordinate the physical laws with which physical experiment makes us acquainted, the enunciation of which, without the aid of mathematics, we should be unable to effect. Whether the ether exists or not matters little—let us leave that to the metaphysicians; what is essential for us is, that everything happens as if it existed, and that this hypothesis is found to be suitable for the explanation of phenomena. After all, have we any other

[1] This chapter is mainly taken from the prefaces of two of my books—*Théorie Mathématique de la lumière* (Paris: Naud, 1889), and *Électricité et Optique* (Paris: Naud, 1901).

reason for believing in the existence of material objects? That, too, is only a convenient hypothesis; only, it will never cease to be so, while some day, no doubt, the ether will be thrown aside as useless.

But at the present moment the laws of optics, and the equations which translate them into the language of analysis, hold good—at least as a first approximation. It will therefore be always useful to study a theory which brings these equations into connection.

The undulatory theory is based on a molecular hypothesis; this is an advantage to those who think they can discover the cause under the law. But others find in it a reason for distrust; and this distrust seems to me as unfounded as the illusions of the former. These hypotheses play but a secondary rôle. They may be sacrificed, and the sole reason why this is not generally done is, that it would involve a certain loss of lucidity in the explanation. In fact, if we look at it a little closer we shall see that we borrow from molecular hypotheses but two things—the principle of the conservation of energy, and the linear form of the equations, which is the general law of small movements as of all small variations. This explains why most of the conclusions of Fresnel remain unchanged when we adopt the electro-magnetic theory of light.

*Maxwell's Theory.*—We all know that it was Maxwell who connected by a slender tie two branches of physics—optics and electricity—until then unsuspected of having anything in common. Thus blended in a larger aggregate, in a higher harmony, Fresnel's theory of optics did not perish. Parts of it are yet alive, and their mutual relations are still the same. Only, the language which we use to express them has changed; and, on the other hand, Maxwell has revealed to us other relations, hitherto unsuspected, between the different branches of optics and the domain of electricity.

The first time a French reader opens Maxwell's book, his admiration is tempered with a feeling of uneasiness, and often of distrust.

It is only after prolonged study, and at the cost of much effort, that this feeling disappears. Some minds of high calibre never lose this feeling. Why is it so difficult for the ideas of this English scientist to become acclimatised among us? No doubt the education received by most enlightened Frenchmen predisposes them to appreciate precision and logic more than any other qualities. In this respect the old theories of mathematical physics gave us complete satisfaction. All our masters, from Laplace to Cauchy, proceeded along the same lines. Starting with clearly enunciated hypotheses, they deduced from them all their consequences with mathematical rigour, and then compared them with experiment. It seemed to be their aim to give to each of the branches of physics the same precision as to celestial mechanics.

A mind accustomed to admire such models is not easily satisfied with a theory.  Not only will it not tolerate the least appearance of contradiction, but it will expect the different parts to be logically connected with one another, and will require the number of hypotheses to be reduced to a minimum.

This is not all; there will be other demands which appear to me to be less reasonable.  Behind the matter of which our senses are aware, and which is made known to us by experiment, such a thinker will expect to see another kind of matter —the only true matter in its opinion—which will no longer have anything but purely geometrical qualities, and the atoms of which will be mathematical points subject to the laws of dynamics alone.  And yet he will try to represent to himself, by an unconscious contradiction, these invisible and colourless atoms, and therefore to bring them as close as possible to ordinary matter.

Then only will he be thoroughly satisfied, and he will then imagine that he has penetrated the secret of the universe.  Even if the satisfaction is fallacious, it is none the less difficult to give it up.  Thus, on opening the pages of Maxwell, a Frenchman expects to find a theoretical whole, as logical and as precise as the physical optics that is founded on the hypothesis of the ether.  He is thus preparing for himself a disappointment which I should like the reader to avoid; so I will warn him at once of what he will find and what he will not find in Maxwell.

Maxwell does not give a mechanical explanation of electricity and magnetism; he confines himself to showing that such an explanation is possible. He shows that the phenomena of optics are only a particular case of electro-magnetic phenomena. From the whole theory of electricity a theory of light can be immediately deduced. Unfortunately the converse is not true; it is not always easy to find a complete explanation of electrical phenomena. In particular it is not easy if we take as our starting-point Fresnel's theory; to do so, no doubt, would be impossible; but none the less we must ask ourselves if we are compelled to surrender admirable results which we thought we had definitively acquired. That seems a step backwards, and many sound intellects will not willingly allow of this.

Should the reader consent to set some bounds to his hopes, he will still come across other difficulties. The English scientist does not try to erect a unique, definitive, and well-arranged building; he seems to raise rather a large number of provisional and independent constructions, between which communication is difficult and sometimes impossible. Take, for instance, the chapter in which electrostatic attractions are explained by the pressures and tensions of the dielectric medium. This chapter might be suppressed without the rest of the book being thereby less clear or less complete, and yet it contains a theory which is self-sufficient, and which can be understood without reading a word of what precedes or follows. But it is not only independent of the rest of the book; it is difficult to reconcile it with the fundamental ideas of the volume. Maxwell does not even attempt to reconcile it; he merely says: "I have not been able to make the next step—namely, to account by mechanical considerations for these stresses in the dielectric."

This example will be sufficient to show what I mean; I could quote many others. Thus, who would suspect on reading the pages devoted to magnetic rotatory polarisation that there is an identity between optical and magnetic phenomena?

We must not flatter ourselves that we have avoided every contradiction, but we ought to make up our minds. Two contradictory theories, provided that they are kept from overlapping, and that we do not look to find in them the explanation of things, may, in fact, be very useful instruments of research; and perhaps the reading of Maxwell would be less suggestive if he had not opened up to us so many new and divergent ways. But the fundamental idea is masked, as it were. So far is this the case, that in most works that are popularised, this idea is the only point which is left completely untouched. To show the importance of this, I think I ought to explain in what this fundamental idea consists; but for that purpose a short digression is necessary.

*The Mechanical Explanation of Physical Phenomena.* —In every physical phenomenon there is a certain number of parameters which are reached directly by experiment, and which can be measured. I shall call them the parameters $q$. Observation next teaches us the laws of the variations of these parameters, and these laws can be generally stated in the form of differential equations which connect together the parameters $q$ and time. What can be done to give a mechanical interpretation to such a phenomenon? We may endeavour to explain it, either by the movements of ordinary matter, or by those of one or more hypothetical fluids. These fluids will be considered as formed of a very large number of isolated molecules $m$. When may we say that we have a complete mechanical explanation of the phenomenon? It will be, on the one hand, when we know the differential equations which are satisfied by the co-ordinates of these hypothetical molecules $m$, equations which must, in addition, conform to the laws of dynamics; and, on the other hand, when we know the relations which define the co-ordinates of the molecules $m$ as functions of the parameters $q$, attainable by experiment. These equations, as I have said, should conform to the principles of dynamics, and, in particular, to the principle of the conservation of energy, and to that of least action.

The first of these two principles teaches us that the total energy is constant, and may be divided into two parts:

(1) Kinetic energy, or *vis viva*, which depends on the masses of the hypothetical molecules $m$, and on their velocities. This I shall call T. (2) The potential energy which depends only on the co-ordinates of these molecules, and this I shall call U. It is the sum of the energies T and U that is constant.

Now what are we taught by the principle of least action? It teaches us that to pass from the initial position occupied at the instant $t_0$ to the final position occupied at the instant $t_1$, the system must describe such a path that in the interval of time between the instant $t_0$ and $t_1$, the mean value of the action—*i.e.*, the *difference* between the two energies T and U, must be as small as possible. The first of these two principles is, moreover, a consequence of the second. If we know the functions T and U, this second principle is sufficient to determine the equations of motion.

Among the paths which enable us to pass from one position to another, there is clearly one for which the mean value of the action is smaller than for all the others. In addition, there is only such path; and it follows from this, that the principle of least action is sufficient to determine the path followed, and therefore the equations of motion. We thus obtain what are called the equations of Lagrange. In these equations the independent variables are the co-ordinates of the hypothetical molecules $m$; but I now assume that we take for the variables the parameters $q$, which are directly accessible to experiment.

The two parts of the energy should then be expressed as a function of the parameters $q$ and their derivatives; it is clear that it is under this form that they will appear to the experimenter. The latter will naturally endeavour to define kinetic and potential energy by the aid of quantities he can directly observe.[1] If this be granted, the system will always proceed from one position to another by such a path that the mean value of the action is a minimum. It matters little that T and U are now expressed by the aid of the parameters $q$ and their derivatives; it matters little that it is also by the aid of these parameters that we define the initial and final positions; the principle of least action will always remain true.

Now here again, of the whole of the paths which lead from one position to another, there is one and only one for which the mean action is a minimum. The principle of least action is therefore sufficient for the determination of the differential equations which define the variations of the parameters $q$. The equations thus obtained are another form of Lagrange's equations.

---

[1] We may add that U will depend only on the $q$ parameters, that T will depend on them and their derivatives with respect to time, and will be a homogeneous polynomial of the second degree with respect to these derivatives.

To form these equations we need not know the relations which connect the parameters $q$ with the co-ordinates of the hypothetical molecules, nor the masses of the molecules, nor the expression of U as a function of the co-ordinates of these molecules. All we need know is the expression of U as a function of the parameters $q$, and that of T as a function of the parameters $q$ and their derivatives —*i.e.*, the expressions of the kinetic and potential energy in terms of experimental data.

One of two things must now happen. Either for a convenient choice of T and U the Lagrangian equations, constructed as we have indicated, will be identical with the differential equations deduced from experiment, or there will be no functions T and U for which this identity takes place. In the latter case it is clear that no mechanical explanation is possible. The *necessary* condition for a mechanical explanation to be possible is therefore this: that we may choose the functions T and U so as to satisfy the principle of least action, and of the conservation of energy. Besides, this condition is *sufficient*. Suppose, in fact, that we have found a function U of the parameters $q$, which represents one of the parts of energy, and that the part of the energy which we represent by T is a function of the parameters $q$ and their derivatives; that it is a polynomial of the second degree with respect to its derivatives, and finally that the Lagrangian equations formed by the aid of these two functions T and U are in conformity with the data of the experiment. How can we deduce from this a mechanical explanation? U must be regarded as the potential energy of a system of which T is the kinetic energy. There is no difficulty as far as U is concerned, but can T be regarded as the *vis viva* of a material system?

It is easily shown that this is always possible, and in an unlimited number of ways. I will be content with referring the reader to the pages of the preface of my *Électricité et Optique* for further details. Thus, if the principle of least action cannot be satisfied, no mechanical explanation is possible; if it can be satisfied, there is not only one explanation, but an unlimited number, whence it follows that since there is one there must be an unlimited number.

One more remark. Among the quantities that may be reached by experiment directly we shall consider some as the co-ordinates of our hypothetical molecules, some will be our parameters $q$, and the rest will be regarded as dependent not only on the co-ordinates but on the velocities—or what comes to the same thing, we look on them as derivatives of the parameters $q$, or as combinations of these parameters and their derivatives.

Here then a question occurs: among all these quantities measured experimentally which shall we choose to represent the parameters $q$? and which shall we prefer to regard as the derivatives of these parameters? This choice remains arbitrary to a large extent, but a mechanical explanation will be possible if it is done so as to satisfy the principle of least action.

Next, Maxwell asks: Can this choice and that of the two energies T and U be made so that electric phenomena will satisfy this principle? Experiment shows us that the energy of an electro-magnetic field decomposes into electro-static and electro-dynamic energy. Maxwell recognised that if we regard the former as the potential energy U, and the latter as the kinetic energy T, and that if on the other hand we take the electro-static charges of the conductors as the parameters $q$, and the intensity of the currents as derivatives of other parameters $q$—under these conditions, Maxwell has recognised that electric phenomena satisfies the principle of least action. He was then certain of a mechanical explanation. If he had expounded this theory at the beginning of his first volume, instead of relegating it to a corner of the second, it would not have escaped the attention of most readers. If therefore a phenomenon allows of a complete mechanical explanation, it allows of an unlimited number of others, which will equally take into account all the particulars revealed by experiment. And this is confirmed by the history of every branch of physics. In Optics, for instance, Fresnel believed vibration to be perpendicular to the plane of polarisation; Neumann holds that it is parallel to that plane. For a long time an *experimentum crucis* was sought for, which would enable us to decide between these two theories, but in

vain.  In the same way, without going out of the
domain of electricity, we find that the theory of
two fluids and the single fluid theory equally
account in a satisfactory manner for all the laws
of electro-statics.  All these facts are easily explained, thanks to the properties of the Lagrange
equations.

It is easy now to understand Maxwell's fundamental idea.  To demonstrate the possibility of a
mechanical explanation of electricity we need not
trouble to find the explanation itself; we need only
know the expression of the two functions T and U,
which are the two parts of energy, and to form with
these two functions Lagrange's equations, and
then to compare these equations with the experimental laws.

How shall we choose from all the possible
explanations one in which the help of experiment
will be wanting?  The day will perhaps come
when physicists will no longer concern themselves
with questions which are inaccessible to positive
methods, and will leave them to the metaphysicians.  That day has not yet come; man does not
so easily resign himself to remaining for ever ignorant of the causes of things.  Our choice cannot be
therefore any longer guided by considerations in
which personal appreciation plays too large a part.
There are, however, solutions which all will reject
because of their fantastic nature, and others which
all will prefer because of their simplicity.  As
far as magnetism and electricity are concerned,

Maxwell abstained from making any choice. It is not that he has a systematic contempt for all that positive methods cannot reach, as may be seen from the time he has devoted to the kinetic theory of gases. I may add that if in his *magnum opus* he develops no complete explanation, he has attempted one in an article in the *Philosophical Magazine*. The strangeness and the complexity of the hypotheses he found himself compelled to make, led him afterwards to withdraw it.

The same spirit is found throughout his whole work. He throws into relief the essential—*i.e.*, what is common to all theories; everything that suits only a particular theory is passed over almost in silence. The reader therefore finds himself in the presence of form nearly devoid of matter, which at first he is tempted to take as a fugitive and unassailable phantom. But the efforts he is thus compelled to make force him to think, and eventually he sees that there is often something rather artificial in the theoretical "aggregates" which he once admired.

# CHAPTER XIII.

## ELECTRO-DYNAMICS.

THE history of electro-dynamics is very instructive from our point of view. The title of Ampère's immortal work is, *Théorie des phénomènes electro-dynamiques, uniquement fondée sur expérience.* He therefore imagined that he had made no hypotheses; but as we shall not be long in recognising, he was mistaken; only, of these hypotheses he was quite unaware. On the other hand, his successors see them clearly enough, because their attention is attracted by the weak points in Ampère's solution. They made fresh hypotheses, but this time deliberately. How many times they had to change them before they reached the classic system, which is perhaps even now not quite definitive, we shall see.

I. *Ampère's Theory.*—In Ampère's experimental study of the mutual action of currents, he has operated, and he could operate only, with closed currents. This was not because he denied the existence or possibility of open currents. If two conductors are positively and negatively charged and brought into communication by a wire, a current is set up which passes from one to the other until the two potentials are equal. According to the ideas of Ampère's time, this was considered to be an open current; the current was known to pass from the first conductor to the second, but they did not know it returned from the second to the first. All currents of this kind were therefore considered by Ampère to be open currents—for instance, the currents of discharge of a condenser; he was unable to experiment on them, their duration being too short. Another kind of open current may be imagined. Suppose we have two conductors A and B connected by a wire AMB. Small conducting masses in motion are first of all placed in contact with the conductor B, receive an electric charge, and leaving B are set in motion along a path BNA, carrying their charge with them. On coming into contact with A they lose their charge, which then returns to B along the wire AMB. Now here we have, in a sense, a closed circuit, since the electricity describes the closed circuit BNAMB; but the two parts of the current are quite different. In the wire AMB the electricity is displaced *through* a fixed conductor like a voltaic current, overcoming an ohmic resistance and developing heat; we say that it is displaced by *conduction*. In the part BNA the electricity is *carried* by a moving conductor, and is said to be displaced by *convection*. If therefore the convection current is considered to be perfectly analogous to the conduction current, the circuit BNAMB is closed; if on the contrary the convection current is not a "true current," and, for instance, does not act on the magnet, there is only the conduction current AMB, which is *open*. For example, if we connect by a wire the poles of a Holtz machine, the charged rotating disc transfers the electricity by convection from one pole to the other, and it returns to the first pole by conduction through the wire. But currents of this kind are very difficult to produce with appreciable intensity; in fact, with the means at Ampère's disposal we may almost say it was impossible.

To sum up, Ampère could conceive of the existence of two kinds of open currents, but he could experiment on neither, because they were not strong enough, or because their duration was too short. Experiment therefore could only show him the action of a closed current on a closed current— or more accurately, the action of a closed current on a portion of current, because a current can be made to describe a *closed* circuit, of which part may be in motion and the other part fixed. The displacements of the moving part may be studied under the action of another closed current. On the other hand, Ampère had no means of studying the action of an open current either on a closed or on another open current.

1. *The Case of Closed Currents.*—In the case of the mutual action of two closed currents, experiment revealed to Ampère remarkably simple laws. The following will be useful to us in the sequel :—

(1) *If the intensity of the currents is kept constant,* and if the two circuits, after having undergone any displacements and deformations whatever, return finally to their initial positions, the total work done by the electro-dynamical actions is zero. In other words, there is an *electro-dynamical potential* of the two circuits proportional to the product of their intensities, and depending on the form and relative positions of the circuits; the work done by the electro-dynamical actions is equal to the change of this potential.

(2) The action of a closed solenoid is zero.

(3) The action of a circuit C on another voltaic circuit C′ depends only on the "magnetic field" developed by the circuit C. At each point in space we can, in fact, define in magnitude and direction a certain force called "magnetic force," which enjoys the following properties:—

(*a*) The force exercised by C on a magnetic pole is applied to that pole, and is equal to the magnetic force multiplied by the magnetic mass of the pole.

(*b*) A very short magnetic needle tends to take the direction of the magnetic force, and the couple to which it tends to reduce is proportional to the product of the magnetic force, the magnetic moment of the needle, and the sine of the dip of the needle.

(*c*) If the circuit C′ is displaced, the amount of the work done by the electro-dynamic action of C on C′ will be equal to the increment of "flow of magnetic force" which passes through the circuit.

2. *Action of a Closed Current on a Portion of Current.*—Ampère being unable to produce the open current properly so called, had only one way of studying the action of a closed current on a portion of current. This was by operating on a circuit C composed of two parts, one movable and the other fixed. The movable part was, for instance, a movable wire $\alpha\beta$, the ends $\alpha$ and $\beta$ of which could slide along a fixed wire. In one of the positions of the movable wire the end $\alpha$ rested on the point A, and the end $\beta$ on the point B of the fixed wire. The current ran from $\alpha$ to $\beta$—*i.e.*, from A to B along the movable wire, and then from B to A along the fixed wire. *This current was therefore closed.*

In the second position, the movable wire having slipped, the points $\alpha$ and $\beta$ were respectively at A′ and B′ on the fixed wire. The current ran from $\alpha$ to $\beta$—*i.e.*, from A′ to B′ on the movable wire, and returned from B′ to B, and then from B to A, and then from A to A′—all on the fixed wire. This current was also closed. If a similar circuit be exposed to the action of a closed current C, the movable part will be displaced just as if it were acted on by a force. Ampère *admits* that the force, apparently acting on the movable part A B, representing the action of C on the portion $\alpha\beta$ of the current, remains the same whether an open current runs through $\alpha\beta$, stopping at α and β, or whether a closed current runs first to β, and then returns to α through the fixed portion of the circuit. This hypothesis seemed natural enough, and Ampère innocently assumed it; nevertheless the hypothesis *is not a necessity*, for we shall presently see that Helmholtz rejected it. However that may be, it enabled Ampère, although he had never produced an open current, to lay down the laws of the action of a closed current on an open current, or even on an element of current. They are simple:

(1) The force acting on an element of current is applied to that element; it is normal to the element and to the magnetic force, and proportional to that component of the magnetic force which is normal to the element.

(2) The action of a closed solenoid on an element of current is zero. But the electrodynamic potential has disappeared—*i.e.*, when a closed and an open current of constant intensities return to their initial positions, the total work done is not zero.

3 *Continuous Rotations.*—The most remarkable electro-dynamical experiments are those in which continuous rotations are produced, and which are called *unipolar induction* experiments. A magnet may turn about its axis; a current passes first through a fixed wire and then enters the magnet by the pole N, for instance, passes through half the magnet, and emerges by a sliding contact and re-enters the fixed wire. The magnet

then begins to rotate continuously. This is Faraday's experiment. How is it possible? If it were a question of two circuits of invariable form, C fixed and C' movable about an axis, the latter would never take up a position of continuous rotation; in fact, there is an electro-dynamical potential; there must therefore be a position of equilibrium when the potential is a maximum. Continuous rotations are therefore possible only when the circuit C' is composed of two parts— one fixed, and the other movable about an axis, as in the case of Faraday's experiment. Here again it is convenient to draw a distinction. The passage from the fixed to the movable part, or *vice versâ*, may take place either by simple contact, the same point of the movable part remaining constantly in contact with the same point of the fixed part, or by sliding contact, the same point of the movable part coming successively into contact with the different points of the fixed part.

It is only in the second case that there can be continuous rotation. This is what then happens:—the system tends to take up a position of equilibrium; but, when at the point of reaching that position, the sliding contact puts the moving part in contact with a fresh point in the fixed part; it changes the connexions and therefore the conditions of equilibrium, so that as the position of equilibrium is ever eluding, so to speak, the system which is trying to reach it, rotation may take place indefinitely.

Ampère admits that the action of the circuit on the movable part of C′ is the same as if the fixed part of C′ did not exist, and therefore as if the current passing through the movable part were an open current.  He concluded that the action of a closed on an open current, or *vice versâ*, that of an open current on a fixed current, may give rise to continuous rotation.  But this conclusion depends on the hypothesis which I have enunciated, and to which, as I said above, Helmholtz declined to subscribe.

4. *Mutual Action of Two Open Currents.*—As far as the mutual action of two open currents, and in particular that of two elements of current, is concerned, all experiment breaks down.  Ampère falls back on hypothesis.  He assumes: (1) that the mutual action of two elements reduces to a force acting along their *join*; (2) that the action of two closed currents is the resultant of the mutual actions of their different elements, which are the same as if these elements were isolated.

The remarkable thing is that here again Ampère makes two hypotheses without being aware of it.  However that may be, these two hypotheses, together with the experiments on closed currents, suffice to determine completely the law of mutual action of two elements.  But then, most of the simple laws we have met in the case of closed currents are no longer true.  In the first place, there is no electro-dynamical potential; nor was there any, as we have seen, in the case of a closed current acting on an open current. Next, there is, properly speaking, no magnetic force; and we have above defined this force in three different ways: (1) By the action on a magnetic pole; (2) by the director couple which orientates the magnetic needle; (3) by the action on an element of current.

In the case with which we are immediately concerned, not only are these three definitions not in harmony, but each has lost its meaning:—

(1) A magnetic pole is no longer acted on by a unique force applied to that pole. We have seen, in fact, the action of an element of current on a pole is not applied to the pole but to the element; it may, moreover, be replaced by a force applied to the pole and by a couple.

(2) The couple which acts on the magnetic needle is no longer a simple director couple, for its moment with respect to the axis of the needle is not zero. It decomposes into a director couple, properly so called, and a supplementary couple which tends to produce the continuous rotation of which we have spoken above.

(3) Finally, the force acting on an element of a current is not normal to that element. In other words, *the unity of the magnetic force has disappeared.*

Let us see in what this unity consists. Two systems which exercise the same action on a magnetic pole will also exercise the same action on an indefinitely small magnetic needle, or on an element of current placed at the point in space at which the pole is. Well, this is true if the two systems only contain closed currents, and according to Ampère it would not be true if the systems contained open currents. It is sufficient to remark, for instance, that if a magnetic pole is placed at A and an element at B, the direction of the element being in AB produced, this element, which will exercise no action on the pole, will exercise an action either on a magnetic needle placed at A, or on an element of current at A.

5. *Induction.*—We know that the discovery of electro-dynamical induction followed not long after the immortal work of Ampère. As long as it is only a question of closed currents there is no difficulty, and Helmholtz has even remarked that the principle of the conservation of energy is sufficient for us to deduce the laws of induction from the electro-dynamical laws of Ampère. But on the condition, as Bertrand has shown,—that we make a certain number of hypotheses.

The same principle again enables this deduction to be made in the case of open currents, although the result cannot be tested by experiment, since such currents cannot be produced.

If we wish to compare this method of analysis with Ampère's theorem on open currents, we get results which are calculated to surprise us. In the first place, induction cannot be deduced from the variation of the magnetic field by the well-known formula of scientists and practical men;

in fact, as I have said, properly speaking, there is no magnetic field. But further, if a circuit C is subjected to the induction of a variable voltaic system S, and if this system S be displaced and deformed in any way whatever, so that the intensity of the currents of this system varies according to any law whatever, then so long as after these variations the system eventually returns to its initial position, it seems natural to suppose that the *mean* electro-motive force induced in the current C is zero. This is true if the circuit C is closed, and if the system S only contains closed currents. It is no longer true if we accept the theory of Ampère, since there would be open currents. So that not only will induction no longer be the variation of the flow of magnetic force in any of the usual senses of the word, but it cannot be represented by the variation of that force whatever it may be.

II. *Helmholtz's Theory.*—I have dwelt upon the consequences of Ampère's theory and on his method of explaining the action of open currents. It is difficult to disregard the paradoxical and artificial character of the propositions to which we are thus led. We feel bound to think " it cannot be so." We may imagine then that Helmholtz has been led to look for something else. He rejects the fundamental hypothesis of Ampère—namely, that the mutual action of two elements of current reduces to a force along their join. He admits that an element of current is not acted upon by a single force but by a force and a couple, and this is what gave rise to the celebrated polemic between Bertrand and Helmholtz. Helmholtz replaces Ampère's hypothesis by the following:—Two elements of current always admit of an electro-dynamic potential, depending solely upon their position and orientation; and the work of the forces that they exercise one on the other is equal to the variation of this potential. Thus Helmholtz can no more do without hypothesis than Ampère, but at least he does not do so without explicitly announcing it. In the case of closed currents, which alone are accessible to experiment, the two theories agree; in all other cases they differ. In the first place, contrary to what Ampère supposed, the force which seems to act on the movable portion of a closed current is not the same as that acting on the movable portion if it were isolated and if it constituted an open current. Let us return to the circuit C′, of which we spoke above, and which was formed of a movable wire sliding on a fixed wire. In the only experiment that can be made the movable portion $\alpha \beta$ is not isolated, but is part of a closed circuit. When it passes from AB to A′B′, the total electro-dynamic potential varies for two reasons. First, it has a slight increment because the potential of A′B′ with respect to the circuit C is not the same as that of AB; secondly, it has a second increment because it must be increased by the potentials of the elements

AA' and B'B with respect to C. It is this *double* increment which represents the work of the force acting upon the portion AB. If, on the contrary, αβ be isolated, the potential would only have the first increment, and this first increment alone would measure the work of the force acting on AB. In the second place, there could be no continuous rotation without sliding contact, and in fact, that, as we have seen in the case of closed currents, is an immediate consequence of the existence of an electro-dynamic potential. In Faraday's experiment, if the magnet is fixed, and if the part of the current external to the magnet runs along a movable wire, that movable wire may undergo continuous rotation. But it does not mean that, if the contacts of the weir with the magnet were suppressed, and an open current were to run along the wire, the wire would still have a movement of continuous rotation. I have just said, in fact, that an isolated element is not acted on in the same way as a movable element making part of a closed circuit. But there is another difference. The action of a solenoid on a closed current is zero according to experiment and according to the two theories. Its action on an open current would be zero according to Ampère, and it would not be zero according to Helmholtz. From this follows an important consequence. We have given above three definitions of the magnetic force. The third has no meaning here, since an element of current

is no longer acted upon by a single force. Nor
has the first any meaning. What, in fact, is a
magnetic pole? It is the extremity of an
indefinite linear magnet. This magnet may be
replaced by an indefinite solenoid. For the
definition of magnetic force to have any meaning, the action exercised by an open current on
an indefinite solenoid would only depend on the
position of the extremity of that solenoid—*i.e.,*
that the action of a closed solenoid is zero. Now
we have just seen that this is not the case. On
the other hand, there is nothing to prevent us
from adopting the second definition which is
founded on the measurement of the director
couple which tends to orientate the magnetic
needle; but, if it is adopted, neither the effects
of induction nor electro-dynamic effects will
depend solely on the distribution of the lines
of force in this magnetic field.

III. *Difficulties raised by these Theories.*—Helmholtz's theory is an advance on that of Ampère;
it is necessary, however, that every difficulty
should be removed. In both, the name " magnetic
field " has no meaning, or, if we give it one by a
more or less artificial convention, the ordinary
laws so familiar to electricians no longer apply;
and it is thus that the electro-motive force induced
in a wire is no longer measured by the number
of lines of force met by that wire. And our
objections do not proceed only from the fact that
it is difficult to give up deeply-rooted habits of

language and thought. There is something more. If we do not believe in actions at a distance, electro-dynamic phenomena must be explained by a modification of the medium. And this medium is precisely what we call "magnetic field," and then the electro-magnetic effects should only depend on that field. All these difficulties arise from the hypothesis of open currents.

IV. *Maxwell's Theory.*—Such were the difficulties raised by the current theories, when Maxwell with a stroke of the pen caused them to vanish. To his mind, in fact, all currents are closed currents. Maxwell admits that if in a dielectric, the electric field happens to vary, this dielectric becomes the seat of a particular phenomenon acting on the galvanometer like a current and called the *current of displacement.* If, then, two conductors bearing positive and negative charges are placed in connection by means of a wire, during the discharge there is an open current of conduction in that wire; but there are produced at the same time in the surrounding dielectric currents of displacement which close this current of conduction. We know that Maxwell's theory leads to the explanation of optical phenomena which would be due to extremely rapid electrical oscillations. At that period such a conception was only a daring hypothesis which could be supported by no experiment; but after twenty years Maxwell's ideas received the confirmation of experiment. Hertz succeeded in producing systems of electric oscillations which reproduce all the properties of light, and only differ by the length of their wave—that is to say, as violet differs from red. In some measure he made a synthesis of light. It might be said that Hertz has not directly proved Maxwell's fundamental idea of the action of the current of displacement on the galvanometer. That is true in a sense. What he has shown directly is that electro-magnetic induction is not instantaneously propagated, as was supposed, but its speed is the speed of light. Yet, to suppose there is no current of displacement, and that induction is with the speed of light; or, rather, to suppose that the currents of displacement produce inductive effects, and that the induction takes place instantaneously —*comes to the same thing*. This cannot be seen at the first glance, but it is proved by an analysis of which I must not even think of giving even a summary here.

V. *Rowland's Experiment.*—But, as I have said above, there are two kinds of open conduction currents. There are first the currents of discharge of a condenser, or of any .conductor whatever. There are also cases in which the electric charges describe a closed contour, being displaced by conduction in one part of the circuit and by convection in the other part. The question might be regarded as solved for open currents of the first kind; they were closed by currents of displacement. For open currents of the second kind the solution appeared still more simple.

It seemed that if the current were closed it could only be by the current of convection itself. For that purpose it was sufficient to admit that a "convection current"—*i.e.*, a charged conductor in motion—could act on the galvanometer. But experimental confirmation was lacking. It appeared difficult, in fact, to obtain a sufficient intensity even by increasing as much as possible the charge and the velocity of the conductors. Rowland, an extremely skilful experimentalist, was the first to triumph, or to seem to triumph, over these difficulties. A disc received a strong electrostatic charge and a very high speed of rotation. An astatic magnetic system placed beside the disc underwent deviations. The experiment was made twice by Rowland, once in Berlin and once at Baltimore. It was afterwards repeated by Himstedt. These physicists even believed that they could announce that they had succeeded in making quantitative measurements. For twenty years Rowland's law was admitted without objection by all physicists, and, indeed, everything seemed to confirm it. The spark certainly does produce a magnetic effect, and does it not seem extremely likely that the spark discharged is due to particles taken from one of the electrodes and transferred to the other electrode with their charge? Is not the very spectrum of the spark, in which we recognise the lines of the metal of the electrode, a proof of it? The spark would then be a real current of induction.

On the other hand, it is also admitted that in an electrolyte the electricity is carried by the ions in motion. The current in an electrolyte would therefore also be a current of convection; but it acts on the magnetic needle. And in the same way for cathodic rays; Crooks attributed these rays to very subtle matter charged with negative electricity and moving with very high velocity. He looked upon them, in other words, as currents of convection. Now, these cathodic rays are deviated by the magnet. In virtue of the principle of action and re-action, they should in their turn deviate the magnetic needle. It is true that Hertz believed he had proved that the cathodic rays do not carry negative electricity, and that they do not act on the magnetic needle; but Hertz was wrong. First of all, Perrin succeeded in collecting the electricity carried by these rays— electricity of which Hertz denied the existence; the German scientist appears to have been deceived by the effects due to the action of the X-rays, which were not yet discovered. Afterwards, and quite recently, the action of the cathodic rays on the magnetic needle has been brought to light. Thus all these phenomena looked upon as currents of convection, electric sparks, electrolytic currents, cathodic rays, act in the same manner on the galvanometer and in conformity to Rowland's law.

VI. *Lorentz's Theory.*—We need not go much further. According to Lorentz's theory, currents of conduction would themselves be true convection currents. Electricity would remain indissolubly connected with certain material particles called *electrons*. The circulation of these electrons through bodies would produce voltaic currents, and what would distinguish conductors from insulators would be that the one could be traversed by these electrons, while the others would check the movement of the electrons. Lorentz's theory is very attractive. It gives a very simple explanation of certain phenomena, which the earlier theories—even Maxwell's in its primitive form—could only deal with in an unsatisfactory manner; for example, the aberration of light, the partial impulse of luminous waves, magnetic polarisation, and Zeeman's experiment.

A few objections still remained. The phenomena of an electric system seemed to depend on the absolute velocity of translation of the centre of gravity of this system, which is contrary to the idea that we have of the relativity of space. Supported by M. Crémieu, M. Lippman has presented this objection in a very striking form. Imagine two charged conductors with the same velocity of translation. They are relatively at rest. However, each of them being equivalent to a current of convection, they ought to attract one another, and by measuring this attraction we could measure their absolute velocity. "No!" replied the partisans of Lorentz. "What we could measure in that way is not their absolute velocity, but their relative velocity *with respect to the ether*, so that the principle of relativity is safe." Whatever there may be in these objections, the edifice of electro-dynamics seemed, at any rate in its broad lines, definitively constructed. Everything was presented under the most satisfactory aspect. The theories of Ampère and Helmholtz, which were made for the open currents that no longer existed, seem to have no more than purely historic interest, and the inextricable complications to which these theories led have been almost forgotten. This quiescence has been recently disturbed by the experiments of M. Crémieu, which have contradicted, or at least have seemed to contradict, the results formerly obtained by Rowland. Numerous investigators have endeavoured to solve the question, and fresh experiments have been undertaken. What result will they give? I shall take care not to risk a prophecy which might be falsified between the day this book is ready for the press and the day on which it is placed before the public.

THE END.

# CATALOG OF DOVER BOOKS

# Puzzles, Mathematical Recreations

**SYMBOLIC LOGIC and THE GAME OF LOGIC, Lewis Carroll.** "Symbolic Logic" is not concerned with modern symbolic logic, but is instead a collection of over 380 problems posed with charm and imagination, using the syllogism, and a fascinating diagrammatic method of drawing conclusions. In "The Game of Logic" Carroll's whimsical imagination devises a logical game played with 2 diagrams and counters (included) to manipulate hundreds of tricky syllogisms. The final section, "Hit or Miss" is a lagniappe of 101 additional puzzles in the delightful Carroll manner. Until this reprint edition, both of these books were rarities costing up to $15 each. Symbolic Logic: Index. xxxi + 199pp. The Game of Logic: 96pp. 2 vols. bound as one. 5⅜ x 8.    T492 Paperbound **$1.50**

**PILLOW PROBLEMS and A TANGLED TALE, Lewis Carroll.** One of the rarest of all Carroll's works, "Pillow Problems" contains 72 original math puzzles, all typically ingenious. Particularly fascinating are Carroll's answers which remain exactly as he thought them out, reflecting his actual mental process. The problems in "A Tangled Tale" are in story form, originally appearing as a monthly magazine serial. Carroll not only gives the solutions, but uses answers sent in by readers to discuss wrong approaches and misleading paths, and grades them for insight. Both of these books were rarities until this edition, "Pillow Problems" costing up to $25, and "A Tangled Tale" $15. Pillow Problems: Preface and Introduction by Lewis Carroll. xx + 109pp. A Tangled Tale: 6 illustrations. 152pp. Two vols. bound as one. 5⅜ x 8.    T493 Paperbound **$1.50**

**AMUSEMENTS IN MATHEMATICS, Henry Ernest Dudeney.** The foremost British originator of mathematical puzzles is always intriguing, witty, and paradoxical in this classic, one of the largest collections of mathematical amusements. More than 430 puzzles, problems, and paradoxes. Mazes and games, problems on number manipulation, unicursal and other route problems, puzzles on measuring, weighing, packing, age, kinship, chessboards, joiners', crossing river, plane figure dissection, and many others. Solutions. More than 450 illustrations. vii + 258pp. 5⅜ x 8.    T473 Paperbound **$1.25**

**THE CANTERBURY PUZZLES, Henry Dudeney.** Chaucer's pilgrims set one another problems in story form. Also Adventures of the Puzzle Club, the Strange Escape of the King's Jester, the Monks of Riddlewell, the Squire's Christmas Puzzle Party, and others. All puzzles are original, based on dissecting plane figures, arithmetic, algebra, elementary calculus and other branches of mathematics, and purely logical ingenuity. "The limit of ingenuity and intricacy," The Observer. Over 110 puzzles. Full Solutions. 150 illustrations. vii + 225pp. 5⅜ x 8.    T474 Paperbound **$1.25**

**MATHEMATICAL EXCURSIONS, H. A. Merrill.** Even if you hardly remember your high school math, you'll enjoy the 90 stimulating problems contained in this book and you will come to understand a great many mathematical principles with surprisingly little effort. Many useful shortcuts and diversions not generally known are included: division by inspection, Russian peasant multiplication, memory systems for pi, building odd and even magic squares, square roots by geometry, dyadic systems, and many more. Solutions to difficult problems. 50 illustrations. 145pp. 5⅜ x 8.    T350 Paperbound **$1.00**

**MAGIC SQUARES AND CUBES, W. S. Andrews.** Only book-length treatment in English, a thorough non-technical description and analysis. Here are nasik, overlapping, pandiagonal, serrated squares; magic circles, cubes, spheres, rhombuses. Try your hand at 4-dimensional magical figures! Much unusual folklore and tradition included. High school algebra is sufficient. 754 diagrams and illustrations. viii + 419pp. 5⅜ x 8.    T658 Paperbound **$1.85**

**CALIBAN'S PROBLEM BOOK: MATHEMATICAL, INFERENTIAL AND CRYPTOGRAPHIC PUZZLES, H. Phillips (Caliban), S. T. Shovelton, G. S. Marshall.** 105 ingenious problems by the greatest living creator of puzzles based on logic and inference. Rigorous, modern, piquant; reflecting their author's unusual personality, these intermediate and advanced puzzles all involve the ability to reason clearly through complex situations; some call for mathematical knowledge, ranging from algebra to number theory. Solutions. xi + 180pp. 5⅜ x 8.    T736 Paperbound **$1.25**

**MATHEMATICAL PUZZLES FOR BEGINNERS AND ENTHUSIASTS, G. Mott-Smith.** 188 mathematical puzzles based on algebra, dissection of plane figures, permutations, and probability, that will test and improve your powers of inference and interpretation. The Odic Force, The Spider's Cousin, Ellipse Drawing, theory and strategy of card and board games like tit-tat-toe, go moku, salvo, and many others. 100 pages of detailed mathematical explanations. Appendix of primes, square roots, etc. 135 illustrations. 2nd revised edition. 248pp. 5⅜ x 8.    T198 Paperbound **$1.00**

**MATHEMAGIC, MAGIC PUZZLES, AND GAMES WITH NUMBERS, R. V. Heath.** More than 60 new puzzles and stunts based on the properties of numbers. Easy techniques for multiplying large numbers mentally, revealing hidden numbers magically, finding the date of any day in any year, and dozens more. Over 30 pages devoted to magic squares, triangles, cubes, circles, etc. Edited by J. S. Meyer. 76 illustrations. 128pp. 5⅜ x 8.    T110 Paperbound **$1.00**

# CATALOGUE OF DOVER BOOKS

**MATHEMATICAL RECREATIONS, M. Kraitchik.** One of the most thorough compilations of unusual mathematical problems for beginners and advanced mathematicians. Historical problems from Greek, Medieval, Arabic, Hindu sources. 50 pages devoted to pastimes derived from figurate numbers, Mersenne numbers, Fermat numbers, primes and probability. 40 pages of magic, Euler, Latin, panmagic squares. 25 new positional and permutational games of permanent value: fairy chess, latruncles, reversi, jinx, ruma, lasca, tricolor, tetrachrome, etc. Complete rigorous solutions. Revised second edition. 181 illustrations. 333pp. 5⅜ x 8.
T163 Paperbound **$1.75**

**MATHEMATICAL PUZZLES OF SAM LOYD, selected and edited by M. Gardner.** Choice puzzles by the greatest American puzzle creator and innovator. Selected from his famous collection, "Cyclopedia of Puzzles," they retain the unique style and historical flavor of the originals. There are posers based on arithmetic, algebra, probability, game theory, route tracing, topology, counter, sliding block, operations research, geometrical dissection. Includes the famous "14-15" puzzle which was a national craze, and his "Horse of a Different Color" which sold millions of copies. 117 of his most ingenious puzzles in all, 120 line drawings and diagrams. Solutions. Selected references. xx + 167pp. 5⅜ x 8. T498 Paperbound **$1.00**

**MATHEMATICAL PUZZLES OF SAM LOYD, Vol. II, selected and edited by Martin Gardner.** The outstanding 2nd selection from the great American innovator's "Cyclopedia of Puzzles": speed and distance problems, clock problems, plane and solid geometry, calculus problems, etc. Analytical table of contents that groups the puzzles according to the type of mathematics necessary to solve them. 166 puzzles, 150 original line drawings and diagrams. Selected references. xiv + 177pp. 5⅜ x 8. T709 Paperbound **$1.00**

**ARITHMETICAL EXCURSIONS: AN ENRICHMENT OF ELEMENTARY MATHEMATICS, H. Bowers and J. Bowers.** A lively and lighthearted collection of facts and entertainments for anyone who enjoys manipulating numbers or solving arithmetical puzzles: methods of arithmetic never taught in school, little-known facts about the most simple numbers, and clear explanations of more sophisticated topics; mysteries and folklore of numbers, the "Hin-dog-abic" number system, etc. First publication. Index. 529 numbered problems and diversions, all with answers. Bibliography. 60 figures. xiv + 320pp. 5⅜ x 8. T770 Paperbound **$1.65**

**CRYPTANALYSIS, H. F. Gaines.** Formerly entitled ELEMENTARY CRYPTANALYSIS, this introductory-intermediate level text is the best book in print on cryptograms and their solution. It covers all major techniques of the past, and contains much that is not generally known except to experts. Full details about concealment, substitution, and transposition ciphers; periodic mixed alphabets, multafid, Kasiski and Vigenere methods, Ohaver patterns, Playfair, and scores of other topics. 6 language letter and word frequency appendix. 167 problems, now furnished with solutions. Index. 173 figures. vi + 230pp. 5⅜ x 8.
T97 Paperbound **$1.95**

**CRYPTOGRAPHY, L. D. Smith.** An excellent introductory work on ciphers and their solution, the history of secret writing, and actual methods and problems in such techniques as transposition and substitution. Appendices describe the enciphering of Japanese, the Baconian biliteral cipher, and contain frequency tables and a bibliography for further study. Over 150 problems with solutions. 160pp. 5⅜ x 8. T247 Paperbound **$1.00**

**PUZZLE QUIZ AND STUNT FUN, J. Meyer.** The solution to party doldrums. 238 challenging puzzles, stunts and tricks. Mathematical puzzles like The Clever Carpenter, Atom Bomb; mysteries and deductions like The Bridge of Sighs, The Nine Pearls, Dog Logic; observation puzzles like Cigarette Smokers, Telephone Dial; over 200 others including magic squares, tongue twisters, puns, anagrams, and many others. All problems solved fully. 250pp. 5⅜ x 8.
T337 Paperbound **$1.00**

**101 PUZZLES IN THOUGHT AND LOGIC, C. R. Wylie, Jr.** Brand new problems you need no special knowledge to solve! Take the kinks out of your mental "muscles" and enjoy solving murder problems, the detection of lying fishermen, the logical identification of color by a blindman, and dozens more. Introduction with simplified explanation of general scientific method and puzzle solving. 128pp. 5⅜ x 8. T367 Paperbound **$1.00**

**MY BEST PROBLEMS IN MATHEMATICS, Hubert Phillips ("Caliban").** Only elementary mathematics needed to solve these 100 witty, catchy problems by a master problem creator. Problems on the odds in cards and dice, problems in geometry, algebra, permutations, even problems that require no math at all—just a logical mind, clear thinking. Solutions completely worked out. If you enjoy mysteries, alerting your perceptive powers and exercising your detective's eye, you'll find these cryptic puzzles a challenging delight. Original 1961 publication. 100 puzzles, solutions. x + 107pp. 5⅜ x 8. T91 Paperbound **$1.00**

**MY BEST PUZZLES IN LOGIC AND REASONING, Hubert Phillips ("Caliban").** A new collection of 100 inferential and logical puzzles chosen from the best that have appeared in England, available for first time in U.S. By the most endlessly resourceful puzzle creator now living. All data presented are both necessary and sufficient to allow a single unambiguous answer. No special knowledge is required for problems ranging from relatively simple to completely original one-of-a-kinds. Guaranteed to please beginners and experts of all ages. Original publication. 100 puzzles, full solutions. x + 107pp. 5⅜ x 8. T119 Paperbound **$1.00**

The more difficult books are indicated by an asterisk (*)

# Books Explaining Science and Mathematics

**WHAT IS SCIENCE?, N. Campbell.** The role of experiment and measurement, the function of mathematics, the nature of scientific laws, the difference between laws and theories, the limitations of science, and many similarly provocative topics are treated clearly and without technicalities by an eminent scientist. "Still an excellent introduction to scientific philosophy," H. Margenau in PHYSICS TODAY. "A first-rate primer . . . deserves a wide audience," SCIENTIFIC AMERICAN. 192pp. 5⅜ x 8.     S43 Paperbound **$1.25**

**THE NATURE OF PHYSICAL THEORY, P. W. Bridgman.** A Nobel Laureate's clear, non-technical lectures on difficulties and paradoxes connected with frontier research on the physical sciences. Concerned with such central concepts as thought, logic, mathematics, relativity, probability, wave mechanics, etc. he analyzes the contributions of such men as Newton, Einstein, Bohr, Heisenberg, and many others. "Lucid and entertaining . . . recommended to anyone who wants to get some insight into current philosophies of science," THE NEW PHILOSOPHY. Index. xi + 138pp. 5⅜ x 8.     S33 Paperbound **$1.25**

**EXPERIMENT AND THEORY IN PHYSICS, Max Born.** A Nobel Laureate examines the nature of experiment and theory in theoretical physics and analyzes the advances made by the great physicists of our day: Heisenberg, Einstein, Bohr, Planck, Dirac, and others. The actual process of creation is detailed step-by-step by one who participated. A fine examination of the scientific method at work. 44pp. 5⅜ x 8.     S308 Paperbound **75¢**

**THE PSYCHOLOGY OF INVENTION IN THE MATHEMATICAL FIELD, J. Hadamard.** The reports of such men as Descartes, Pascal, Einstein, Poincaré, and others are considered in this investigation of the method of idea-creation in mathematics and other sciences and the thinking process in general. How do ideas originate? What is the role of the unconscious? What is Poincaré's forgetting hypothesis? are some of the fascinating questions treated. A penetrating analysis of Einstein's thought processes concludes the book. xiii + 145pp. 5⅜ x 8.     T107 Paperbound **$1.25**

**THE NATURE OF LIGHT AND COLOUR IN THE OPEN AIR, M. Minnaert.** Why are shadows sometimes blue, sometimes green, or other colors depending on the light and surroundings? What causes mirages? Why do multiple suns and moons appear in the sky? Professor Minnaert explains these unusual phenomena and hundreds of others in simple, easy-to-understand terms based on optical laws and the properties of light and color. No mathematics is required but artists, scientists, students, and everyone fascinated by these "tricks" of nature will find thousands of useful and amazing pieces of information. Hundreds of observational experiments are suggested which require no special equipment. 200 illustrations; 42 photos. xvi + 362pp. 5⅜ x 8.     T196 Paperbound **$1.95**

**THE UNIVERSE OF LIGHT, W. Bragg.** Sir William Bragg, Nobel Laureate and great modern physicist, is also well known for his powers of clear exposition. Here he analyzes all aspects of light for the layman: lenses, reflection, refraction, the optics of vision, x-rays, the photoelectric effect, etc. He tells you what causes the color of spectra, rainbows, and soap bubbles, how magic mirrors work, and much more. Dozens of simple experiments are described. Preface. Index. 199 line drawings and photographs, including 2 full-page color plates. x + 283pp. 5⅜ x 8.     T538 Paperbound **$1.85**

**SOAP-BUBBLES: THEIR COLOURS AND THE FORCES THAT MOULD THEM, C. V. Boys.** For continuing popularity and validity as scientific primer, few books can match this volume of easily-followed experiments, explanations. Lucid exposition of complexities of liquid films, surface tension and related phenomena, bubbles' reaction to heat, motion, music, magnetic fields. Experiments with capillary attraction, soap bubbles on frames, composite bubbles, liquid cylinders and jets, bubbles other than soap, etc. Wonderful introduction to scientific method, natural laws that have many ramifications in areas of modern physics. Only complete edition in print. New Introduction by S. Z. Lewin, New York University. 83 illustrations; 1 full-page color plate. xii + 190pp. 5⅜ x 8½.     T542 Paperbound **95¢**

ES AND THEIR BUILDERS, D. B. Steinman & S. R. Watson. Engineers, historians, and
person who has ever been fascinated by great spans will find this book an endless
of information and interest. Greek and Roman structures, Medieval bridges, modern
such as the Brooklyn Bridge, and the latest developments in the science are retold
of the world's leading authorities on bridge design and construction. BRIDGES AND
BUILDERS is the only comprehensive and accurate semi-popular history of these im-
measures of progress in print. New, greatly revised, enlarged edition. 23 photos; 26
wings. Index. xvii + 401pp. 5⅜ x 8.                                    T431 Paperbound **$2.00**

BRIDGES OF THE WORLD, D. B. Steinman. An up-to-the-minute new edition of a book
ains the fascinating drama of how the world's great bridges came to be built. The
esigner of the famed Mackinac bridge, discusses bridges from all periods and all parts
rld, explaining their various types of construction, and describing the problems their
aced. Although primarily for youngsters, this cannot fail to interest readers of all
Illustrations in the text. 23 photographs. 99pp. 6⅛ x 9¼.              T161 Paperbound **$1.00**

U USE A SLIDE RULE? by A. A. Merrill. A step-by-step explanation of the slide rule
ts the fundamental rules clearly enough for the non-mathematician to understand.
instruction manuals, this work concentrates on the two most important operations:
n and division. 10 easy lessons, each with a clear drawing, for the reader who has
owing other expositions. 1st publication. Index. 2 Appendices. 10 illustrations. 78
with answers. vi + 36 pp. 6⅛ x 9¼.                                    T62 Paperbound **60¢**

CULATE QUICKLY, H. Sticker. A tried and true method for increasing your "num-
the ability to see relationships between numbers and groups of numbers. Addi-
ion, multiplication, division, fractions, and other topics are treated through
generally taught in schools: left to right multiplication, division by inspection,
ot a collection of tricks which work only on special numbers, but a detailed
urse, consisting of over 9,000 problems that you can work in spare moments.
for anyone who is inconvenienced by slow computational skills. 5 or 10
book daily will double or triple your calculation speed. 9,000 problems,
5⅜ x 8.                                                               T295 Paperbound **$1.00**

FUN, GAMES AND PUZZLES, Jack Frohlichstein. A valuable service for parents
have trouble with math, for teachers in need of a supplement to regular
and junior high math texts (each section is graded—easy, average, difficult
tation to different levels of ability), and for just anyone who would like to
lls in an informal and entertaining manner. The author combines ten years
a junior high school math teacher with a method that uses puzzles and
ce the basic ideas and operations of arithmetic. Stress on everyday uses
stock market, personal budgets, insurance, taxes. Intellectually stimulating
418 problems and diversions with answers. Bibliography. 120 illustrations.
x 8½.                                                                 T789 Paperbound **$1.75**

ODERN MATHEMATICS: THEIR NATURE AND USE, Jagjit Singh. Reader with
th will understand main mathematical ideas of modern physics, astronomy,
, evolution, etc. better than many who use them as tools, but compre-
basic structure. Author uses his wide knowledge of non-mathematical
osition of differential equations, matrices, group theory, logic, statistics,
atical foundations, imaginary numbers, vectors, etc. Original publication.
xes. 65 illustr. 322pp. 5⅜ x 8.                                       S587 Paperbound **$1.65**

TION, O. G. Sutton. Everyone with a command of high school algebra will
the finest possible introductions to the application of mathematics to
tics, numerical analysis, waves and wavelike phenomena, Fourier series,
flow and aerodynamics, statistical measures, and meteorology are dis-
larity. Some calculus and differential equations theory is developed by
r's help in the more difficult sections. 88 figures. Index. viii + 236pp.
                                                                      T440 Clothbound **$3.50**

MBOLIC LOGIC AND ITS APPLICATIONS, Rudolph Carnap. One of the
ensive, and rigorous introductions to modern symbolic logic, by per-
master. Not merely elementary theory, but demonstrated applications
and biology. Symbolic languages of various degrees of complexity
onstructed. "A creation of the rank of a masterpiece," Zentralblatt
e Grenzgebiete. Over 300 exercises. 5 figures. Bibliography. Index.
                                                                      S453 Paperbound **$1.85**

OR STUDENTS OF CHEMISTRY AND PHYSICS, J. W. Mellor. Not ab-
ing its problems from familiar laboratory material, this book covers
differential calculus, analytic geometry, functions with singularities,
series, solution of numerical equations, differential equations,
nsions, probability and the theory of errors, calculus of variations,
reader is not familiar with this book, it will repay him to examine
NEWS. 800 problems. 189 figures. 2 appendices; 30 tables of
ns, etc. Bibliography. xxi + 641pp. 5⅜ x 8.                           S193 Paperbound **$2.00**

THE STORY OF X-RAYS FROM RONTGEN TO ISOTOPES, A. R. Bleich, M.D. This book, by a member of the American College of Radiology, gives the scientific explanation of x-rays, their
applications in medicine, industry and art, and their danger (and that of atmospheric radiation) to the individual and the species. You learn how radiation therapy is applied against
cancer, how x-rays diagnose heart disease and other ailments, how they are used to examine
mummies for information on diseases of early societies, and industrial materials for hidden
weaknesses. 54 illustrations show x-rays of flowers, bones, stomach, gears with flaws, etc.
1st publication. Index. xix + 186pp. 5⅜ x 8.                          T622 Paperbound **$1.35**

SPINNING TOPS AND GYROSCOPIC MOTION, John Perry. A classic elementary text of the
dynamics of rotation — the behavior and use of rotating bodies such as gyroscopes and tops.
In simple, everyday English you are shown how quasi-rigidity is induced in discs of paper,
smoke rings, chains, etc., by rapid motions; why a gyrostat falls and why a top rises;
precession; how the earth's motion affects climate; and many other phenomena. Appendix on
practical use of gyroscopes. 62 figures. 128pp. 5⅜ x 8.               T416 Paperbound **$1.00**

SNOW CRYSTALS, W. A. Bentley, M. J. Humphreys. For almost 50 years W. A. Bentley photo-
graphed snow flakes in his laboratory in Jericho, Vermont; in 1931 the American Meteorologi-
cal Society gathered together the best of his work, some 2400 photographs of snow flakes,
plus a few ice flowers, windowpane frosts, dew, frozen rain, and other ice formations.
Pictures were selected for beauty and scientific value. A very valuable work to anyone in
meteorology, cryology; most interesting to layman; extremely useful for artist who wants
beautiful, crystalline designs. All copyright free. Unabridged reprint of 1931 edition. 2453
illustrations. 227pp. 8 x 10½.                                        T287 Paperbound **$2.95**

A DOVER SCIENCE SAMPLER, edited by George Barkin. A collection of brief, non-technical
passages from 44 Dover Books Explaining Science for the enjoyment of the science-minded
browser. Includes work of Bertrand Russell, Poincaré, Laplace, Max Born, Galileo, Newton;
material on physics, mathematics, metallurgy, anatomy, astronomy, chemistry, etc. You will
be fascinated by Martin Gardner's analysis of the sincere pseudo-scientist, Moritz's account
of Newton's absentmindedness, Bernard's examples of human vivisection, etc. Illustrations
from the Diderot Pictorial Encyclopedia and De Re Metallica. 64 pages.                **FREE**

THE STORY OF ATOMIC THEORY AND ATOMIC ENERGY, J. G. Feinberg. A broader approach to
subject of nuclear energy and its cultural implications than any other similar source. Very
readable, informal, completely non-technical text. Begins with first atomic theory, 600 B.C.
and carries you through the work of Mendelejeff, Röntgen, Madame Curie, to Einstein's equation and the A-bomb. New chapter goes through thermonuclear fission, binding energy,
other events up to 1959. Radioactive decay and radiation hazards, future benefits, work of
Bohr, moderns, hundreds more topics. "Deserves special mention . . . not only authoritative
but thoroughly popular in the best sense of the word," Saturday Review. Formerly, "The
Atom Story." Expanded with new chapter. Three appendixes. Index. 34 illustrations. vii +
243pp. 5⅜ x 8.                                                        T625 Paperbound **$1.45**

THE STRANGE STORY OF THE QUANTUM, AN ACCOUNT FOR THE GENERAL READER OF THE
GROWTH OF IDEAS UNDERLYING OUR PRESENT ATOMIC KNOWLEDGE, B. Hoffmann. Presents
lucidly and expertly, with barest amount of mathematics, the problems and theories which
led to modern quantum physics. Dr. Hoffmann begins with the closing years of the 19th
century, when certain trifling discrepancies were noticed, and with illuminating analogies and
examples takes you through the brilliant concepts of Planck, Einstein, Pauli, Broglie, Bohr,
Schroedinger, Heisenberg, Dirac, Sommerfeld, Feynman, etc. This edition includes a new,
long postscript carrying the story through 1958. "Of the books attempting an account of the
history and contents of our modern atomic physics which have come to my attention, this is
the best," H. Margenau, Yale University, in "American Journal of Physics." 32 tables and line
illustrations. Index. 275pp. 5⅜ x 8.                                  T518 Paperbound **$1.45**

SPACE AND TIME, E. Borel. Written by a versatile mathematician of world renown with his
customary lucidity and precision, this introduction to relativity for the layman presents scores
of examples, analogies, and illustrations that open up new ways of thinking about space and
time. It covers abstract geometry and geographical maps, continuity and topology, the propagation of light, the special theory of relativity, the general theory of relativity, theoretical
researches, and much more. Mathematical notes. 2 Indexes. 4 Appendices. 15 figures.
xvi + 243pp. 5⅜ x 8.                                                  T592 Paperbound **$1.45**

FROM EUCLID TO EDDINGTON: A STUDY OF THE CONCEPTIONS OF THE EXTERNAL WORLD, Sir
Edmund Whittaker. A foremost British scientist traces the development of theories of natural
philosophy from the western rediscovery of Euclid to Eddington, Einstein, Dirac, etc. The
inadequacy of classical physics is contrasted with present day attempts to understand the
physical world through relativity, non-Euclidean geometry, space curvature, wave mechanics,
etc. 5 major divisions of examination: Space; Time and Movement; the Concepts of Classical
Physics; the Concepts of Quantum Mechanics; the Eddington Universe. 212pp. 5⅜ x 8.
                                                                      T491 Paperbound **$1.35**

**\*THE EVOLUTION OF SCIENTIFIC THOUGHT FROM NEWTON TO EINSTEIN, A. d'Abro.** A detailed account of the evolution of classical physics into modern relativistic theory and the concommitant changes in scientific methodology. The breakdown of classical physics in the face of non-Euclidean geometry and the electromagnetic equations is carefully discussed and then an exhaustive analysis of Einstein's special and general theories of relativity and their implications is given. Newton, Riemann, Weyl, Lorentz, Planck, Maxwell, and many others are considered. A non-technical explanation of space, time, electromagnetic waves, etc. as understood today. "Model of semi-popular exposition," NEW REPUBLIC. 21 diagrams. 482pp. 5⅜ x 8.
T2 Paperbound **$2.00**

**EINSTEIN'S THEORY OF RELATIVITY, Max Born.** Nobel Laureate explains Einstein's special and general theories of relativity, beginning with a thorough review of classical physics in simple, non-technical language. Exposition of Einstein's work discusses concept of simultaneity, kinematics, relativity of arbitrary motions, the space-time continuum, geometry of curved surfaces, etc., steering middle course between vague popularizations and complex scientific presentations. 1962 edition revised by author takes into account latest findings, predictions of theory and implications for cosmology, indicates what is being sought in unified field theory. Mathematics very elementary, illustrative diagrams and experiments informative but simple. Revised 1962 edition. Revised by Max Born, assisted by Gunther Leibfried and Walter Biem. Index. 143 illustrations. vii + 376pp. 5⅜ x 8.
S769 Paperbound **$2.00**

**PHILOSOPHY AND THE PHYSICISTS, L. Susan Stebbing.** A philosopher examines the philosophical aspects of modern science, in terms of a lively critical attack on the ideas of Jeans and Eddington. Such basic questions are treated as the task of science, causality, determinism, probability, consciousness, the relation of the world of physics to the world of everyday experience. The author probes the concepts of man's smallness before an inscrutable universe, the tendency to idealize mathematical construction, unpredictability theorems and human freedom, the supposed opposition between 19th century determinism and modern science, and many others. Introduces many thought-stimulating ideas about the implications of modern physical concepts. xvi + 295pp. 5⅜ x 8.
T480 Paperbound **$1.65**

**THE RESTLESS UNIVERSE, Max Born.** A remarkably lucid account by a Nobel Laureate of recent theories of wave mechanics, behavior of gases, electrons and ions, waves and particles, electronic structure of the atom, nuclear physics, and similar topics. "Much more thorough and deeper than most attempts . . . easy and delightful," CHEMICAL AND ENGINEERING NEWS. Special feature: 7 animated sequences of 60 figures each showing such phenomena as gas molecules in motion, the scattering of alpha particles, etc. 11 full-page plates of photographs. Total of nearly 600 illustrations. 351pp. 6⅛ x 9¼.
T412 Paperbound **$2.00**

**THE COMMON SENSE OF THE EXACT SCIENCES, W. K. Clifford.** For 70 years a guide to the basic concepts of scientific and mathematical thought. Acclaimed by scientists and laymen alike, it offers a wonderful insight into concepts such as the extension of meaning of symbols, characteristics of surface boundaries, properties of plane figures, measurement of quantities, vectors, the nature of position, bending of space, motion, mass and force, and many others. Prefaces by Bertrand Russell and Karl Pearson. Critical introduction by James Newman. 130 figures. 249pp. 5⅜ x 8.
T61 Paperbound **$1.60**

**MATTER AND LIGHT, THE NEW PHYSICS, Louis de Broglie.** Non-technical explanations by a Nobel Laureate of electro-magnetic theory, relativity, matter, light and radiation, wave mechanics, quantum physics, philosophy of science, and similar topics. This is one of the simplest yet most accurate introductions to the work of men like Planck, Einstein, Bohr, and others. Only 2 of the 21 chapters require a knowledge of mathematics. 300pp. 5⅜ x 8.
T35 Paperbound **$1.75**

**SCIENCE, THEORY AND MAN, Erwin Schrödinger.** This is a complete and unabridged reissue of SCIENCE AND THE HUMAN TEMPERAMENT plus an additional essay: "What Is an Elementary Particle?" Nobel Laureate Schrödinger discusses such topics as nature of scientific method, the nature of science, chance and determinism, science and society, conceptual models for physical entities, elementary particles and wave mechanics. Presentation is popular and may be followed by most people with little or no scientific training. "Fine practical preparation for a time when laws of nature, human institutions . . . are undergoing a critical examination without parallel," Waldemar Kaempffert, N. Y. TIMES. 192pp. 5⅜ x 8.
T428 Paperbound **$1.35**

**CONCERNING THE NATURE OF THINGS, Sir William Bragg.** The Nobel Laureate physicist in his Royal Institute Christmas Lectures explains such diverse phenomena as the formation of crystals, how uranium is transmuted to lead, the way X-rays work, why a spinning ball travels in a curved path, the reason why bubbles bounce from each other, and many other scientific topics that are seldom explained in simple terms. No scientific background needed—book is easy enough that any intelligent adult or youngster can understand it. Unabridged. 32pp. of photos; 57 figures. xii + 232pp. 5⅜ x 8.
T31 Paperbound **$1.35**

**\*THE RISE OF THE NEW PHYSICS (formerly THE DECLINE OF MECHANISM), A. d'Abro.** This authoritative and comprehensive 2 volume exposition is unique · in scientific publishing. Written for intelligent readers not familiar with higher mathematics, it is the only thorough explanation in non-technical language of modern mathematical-physical theory. Combining both history and exposition, it ranges from classical Newtonian concepts up through the electronic theories of Dirac and Heisenberg, the statistical mechanics of Fermi, and Einstein's relativity theories. "A must for anyone doing serious study in the physical sciences," J. OF FRANKLIN INST. 97 illustrations. 991pp. 2 volumes.
T3 Vol. 1, Paperbound **$2.00**
T4 Vol. 2, Paperbound **$2.00**

**SCIENCE AND HYPOTHESIS, Henri Poincaré.** Creative psychology in s as number, magnitude, space, force, classical mechanics were dev scientist uses them in his thought. Hypothesis in physics, theorie duction by Sir James Larmor. "Few mathematicians have had the b and none is his superior in the gift of clear exposition," E. T. B

**THE VALUE OF SCIENCE, Henri Poincaré.** Many of the mos scientific universalist" conveyed with charm and vigor for b the advanced worker. Discusses the nature of scientific truth, universe or imposed upon it by man, logical thought versus i through the works of Weierstrass, Lie, Klein, Riemann), time a time, simultaneity), Hertz's concept of force, interrelation pure math, values within disciplines of Maxwell, Carnot, M iii + 147pp. 5⅜ x 8.

**THE SKY AND ITS MYSTERIES, E. A. Beet.** One of the of the universe; covers history of astronomy from earli of expanding universe, source of stellar energy, birth possibilities of life on other planets. Discusses effects of stars; methods and tools of astronomers; much mor readable book," London Times. Bibliography. Over 50 star map. Introduction. Index. 238pp. 5¼ x 7½.

**OUT OF THE SKY: AN INTRODUCTION TO METEORITICS.** prehensive introduction to the young science of mete mic matter on our planet from outer space and the the terrestrial environment. Essential facts and majo leading experts. Covers ancient reports of meteors clusters; meteorite showers; tektites; planetoidal over 175 photographs. 22 figures. Bibliography and

**THE REALM OF THE NEBULAE, E. Hubble.** One formulation of concept of "island universes." fication, nature, distances, general types of n tion to modern theories for layman. No math illustrations, photos. Index. iv + 201pp. 5⅜ x

**AN ELEMENTARY SURVEY OF CELESTIAL M** gravitational theory and celestial mechanic principles, including: the ecliptic, the orb covery of Neptune, planetary rotation, the (detailed treatment of Sputnik I), etc. Firs exposition. Follow actual methods of as 58 figures. 165pp. 5⅜ x 8.

**GREAT IDEAS AND THEORIES OF MODE** author's popular "Great Ideas of M technical survey of post-Einstein att origin, age of Universe, possibility cosmology and cosmogony recounter Einstein's concepts of relativity, s theories of Jeans, Eddington; Hoyle scientists. A faithful, comprehensiv extremely well-written text intend 5⅜ x 8½.

**BASIC ELECTRICITY, Bureau of** basic electricity for beginner, l tions, presents coordinated, sys insulators, static electricity, r series and parallel circuits, w tance and inductance, measu as alternating and direct cur Each chapter contains proble algebra. Appendices on sign

**ELEMENTARY METALLURGY** metals and alloys; stress All aspects of production to enter metallurgy, for ground on extremely i graphs, glossary. Great

BRID every source classi by one THEIR portant line-dra

FAMOUS that exp author, of the w builders ages. 48

HOW DO Y that pres Unlike mos multiplicati difficulty fo problems, a

HOW TO CAL ber sense" tion, subtrac techniques no well-planned c It is n It is excellen minutes of th answers. 256pp

MATHEMATICAL of children who upper elementa —for ready adap develop basic sk games to introdu of math: banking, and practical, too xix + 306pp. 5⅜

GREAT IDEAS OF M only high school ma genetics, psycholog hend little of thei fields in brilliant ex problems of mathema 2 appendixes. 2 inde

\*MATHEMATICS IN AC find this book one o physical theory. Ballis group concepts, fluid cussed with unusual c the author for the read 5⅜ x 8.

\*INTRODUCTION TO SY clearest, most compreh haps its greatest living in mathematics, physics are analyzed, and one für Mathematik und lhr xvi + 241pp. 5⅜ x 8.

\*HIGHER MATHEMATICS F stract, but practical, draw theory and application of integral calculus, infinite Fourier's theorem and exte determinants, etc. "If the it," CHEM. & ENGINEERIN integrals, probability functi

# CATALOGUE OF DOVER BOOKS

**THE FOURTH DIMENSION SIMPLY EXPLAINED, edited by Henry P. Manning.** Originally written as entries in contest sponsored by "Scientific American," then published in book form, these 22 essays present easily understood explanations of how the fourth dimension may be studied, the relationship of non-Euclidean geometry to the fourth dimension, analogies to three-dimensional space, some fourth-dimensional absurdities and curiosities, possible measurements and forms in the fourth dimension. In general, a thorough coverage of many of the simpler properties of fourth-dimensional space. Multi-points of view on many of the most important aspects are valuable aid to comprehension. Introduction by Dr. Henry P. Manning gives proper emphasis to points in essays, more advanced account of fourth-dimensional geometry. 82 figures. 251pp. 5⅜ x 8.          T711 Paperbound **$1.35**

**TRIGONOMETRY REFRESHER FOR TECHNICAL MEN, A. A. Klaf.** A modern question and answer text on plane and spherical trigonometry. Part I covers plane trigonometry: angles, quadrants, trigonometrical functions, graphical representation, interpolation, equations, logarithms, solution of triangles, slide rules, etc. Part II discusses applications to navigation, surveying, elasticity, architecture, and engineering. Small angles, periodic functions, vectors, polar coordinates, De Moivre's theorem, fully covered. Part III is devoted to spherical trigonometry and the solution of spherical triangles, with applications to terrestrial and astronomical problems. Special time-savers for numerical calculation. 913 questions answered for you! 1738 problems; answers to odd numbers. 494 figures. 14 pages of functions, formulae. Index. x + 629pp. 5⅜ x 8.          T371 Paperbound **$2.00**

**CALCULUS REFRESHER FOR TECHNICAL MEN. A. A. Klaf.** Not an ordinary textbook but a unique refresher for engineers, technicians, and students. An examination of the most important aspects of differential and integral calculus by means of 756 key questions. Part I covers simple differential calculus: constants, variables, functions, increments, derivatives, logarithms, curvature, etc. Part II treats fundamental concepts of integration: inspection, substitution, transformation, reduction, areas and volumes, mean value, successive and partial integration, double and triple integration. Stresses practical aspects! A 50 page section gives applications to civil and nautical engineering, electricity, stress and strain, elasticity, industrial engineering, and similar fields. 756 questions answered. 556 problems; solutions to odd numbers. 36 pages of constants, formulae. Index. v + 431pp. 5⅜ x 8.
          T370 Paperbound **$2.00**

**PROBABILITIES AND LIFE, Emile Borel.** One of the leading French mathematicians of the last 100 years makes use of certain results of mathematics of probabilities and explains a number of problems that for the most part, are related to everyday living or to illness and death: computation of life expectancy tables, chances of recovery from various diseases, probabilities of job accidents, weather predictions, games of chance, and so on. Emphasis on results not processes, though some indication is made of mathematical proofs. Simple in style, free of technical terminology, limited in scope to everyday situations, it is comprehensible to laymen, fine reading for beginning students of probability. New English translation. Index. Appendix. vi + 87pp. 5⅜ x 8½.          T121 Paperbound **$1.00**

**POPULAR SCIENTIFIC LECTURES, Hermann von Helmholtz.** 7 lucid expositions by a pre-eminent scientific mind: "The Physiological Causes of Harmony in Music," "On the Relation of Optics to Painting," "On the Conservation of Force," "On the Interaction of Natural Forces," "On Goethe's Scientific Researches" into theory of color, "On the Origin and Significance of Geometric Axioms," "On Recent Progress in the Theory of Vision." Written with simplicity of expression, stripped of technicalities, these are easy to understand and delightful reading for anyone interested in science or looking for an introduction to serious study of acoustics or optics. Introduction by Professor Morris Kline, Director, Division of Electromagnetic Research, New York University, contains astute, impartial evaluations. Selected from "Popular Lectures on Scientific Subjects," 1st and 2nd series. xii + 286pp. 5⅜ x 8½.          T799 Paperbound **$1.45**

**SCIENCE AND METHOD, Henri Poincaré.** Procedure of scientific discovery, methodology, experiment, idea-germination—the intellectual processes by which discoveries come into being. Most significant and most interesting aspects of development, application of ideas. Chapters cover selection of facts, chance, mathematical reasoning, mathematics, and logic; Whitehead, Russell, Cantor; the new mechanics, etc. 288pp. 5⅜ x 8.          S222 Paperbound **$1.35**

**HEAT AND ITS WORKINGS, Morton Mott-Smith, Ph.D.** An unusual book; to our knowledge the only middle-level survey of this important area of science. Explains clearly such important concepts as physiological sensation of heat and Weber's law, measurement of heat, evolution of thermometer, nature of heat, expansion and contraction of solids, Boyle's law, specific heat, BTU's and calories, evaporation, Andrews's isothermals, radiation, the relation of heat to light, many more topics inseparable from other aspects of physics. A wide, non-mathematical yet thorough explanation of basic ideas, theories, phenomena for laymen and beginning scientists illustrated by experiences of daily life. Bibliography. 50 illustrations. x + 165pp. 5⅜ x 8½.          T978 Paperbound **$1.00**

# Classics of Science

**THE DIDEROT PICTORIAL ENCYCLOPEDIA OF TRADES AND INDUSTRY, MANUFACTURING AND THE TECHNICAL ARTS IN PLATES SELECTED FROM "L'ENCYCLOPEDIE OU DICTIONNAIRE RAISONNE DES SCIENCES, DES ARTS, ET DES METIERS" OF DENIS DIDEROT,** edited with text by C. Gillispie. The first modern selection of plates from the high point of 18th century French engraving, Diderot's famous Encyclopedia. Over 2000 illustrations on 485 full page plates, most of them original size, illustrating the trades and industries of one of the most fascinating periods of modern history, 18th century France. These magnificent engravings provide an invaluable glimpse into the past for the student of early technology, a lively and accurate social document to students of cultures, an outstanding find to the lover of fine engravings. The plates teem with life, with men, women, and children performing all of the thousands of operations necessary to the trades before and during the early stages of the industrial revolution. Plates are in sequence, and show general operations, closeups of difficult operations, and details of complex machinery. Such important and interesting trades and industries are illustrated as sowing, harvesting, beekeeping, cheesemaking, operating windmills, milling flour, charcoal burning, tobacco processing, indigo, fishing, arts of war, salt extraction, mining, smelting iron, casting iron, steel, extracting mercury, zinc, sulphur, copper, etc., slating, tinning, silverplating, gilding, making gunpowder, cannons, bells, shoeing horses, tanning, papermaking, printing, dying, and more than 40 other categories. 920pp. 9 x 12. Heavy library cloth. T421 Two volume set **$18.50**

**THE PRINCIPLES OF SCIENCE, A TREATISE ON LOGIC AND THE SCIENTIFIC METHOD, W. Stanley Jevons.** Treating such topics as Inductive and Deductive Logic, the Theory of Number, Probability, and the Limits of Scientific Method, this milestone in the development of symbolic logic remains a stimulating contribution to the investigation of inferential validity in the natural and social sciences. It significantly advances Boole's logic, and describes a machine which is a foundation of modern electronic calculators. In his introduction, Ernest Nagel of Columbia University says, "(Jevons) . . . continues to be of interest as an attempt to articulate the logic of scientific inquiry." Index. liii + 786pp. 5⅜ x 8.
S446 Paperbound **$2.98**

**\*DIALOGUES CONCERNING TWO NEW SCIENCES, Galileo Galilei.** A classic of experimental science which has had a profound and enduring influence on the entire history of mechanics and engineering. Galileo based this, his finest work, on 30 years of experimentation. It offers a fascinating and vivid exposition of dynamics, elasticity, sound, ballistics, strength of materials, and the scientific method. Translated by H. Crew and A. de Salvio. 126 diagrams. Index. xxi + 288pp. 5⅜ x 8. S99 Paperbound **$1.75**

**DE MAGNETE, William Gilbert.** This classic work on magnetism founded a new science. Gilbert was the first to use the word "electricity," to recognize mass as distinct from weight, to discover the effect of heat on magnetic bodies; invented an electroscope, differentiated between static electricity and magnetism, conceived of the earth as a magnet. Written by the first great experimental scientist, this lively work is valuable not only as an historical landmark, but as the delightfully easy-to-follow record of a perpetually searching, ingenious mind. Translated by P. F. Mottelay. 25 page biographical memoir. 90 fix. lix + 368pp. 5⅜ x 8. S470 Paperbound **$2.00**

**\*OPTICKS, Sir Isaac Newton.** An enormous storehouse of insights and discoveries on light, reflection, color, refraction, theories of wave and corpuscular propagation of light, optical apparatus, and mathematical devices which have recently been reevaluated in terms of modern physics and placed in the top-most ranks of Newton's work! Foreword by Albert Einstein. Preface by I. B. Cohen of Harvard U. 7 pages of portraits, facsimile pages, letters, etc. cxvi + 412pp. 5⅜ x 8. S205 Paperbound **$2.25**

**A SURVEY OF PHYSICAL THEORY, M. Planck.** Lucid essays on modern physics for the general reader by the Nobel Laureate and creator of the quantum revolution. Planck explains how the new concepts came into being; explores the clash between theories of mechanics, electrodynamics, and thermodynamics; and traces the evolution of the concept of light through Newton, Huygens, Maxwell, and his own quantum theory, providing unparalleled insights into his development of this momentous modern concept. Bibliography. Index. vii + 121pp. 5⅜ x 8.
S650 Paperbound **$1.15**

**A SOURCE BOOK IN MATHEMATICS, D. E. Smith.** English translations of the original papers that announced the great discoveries in mathematics from the Renaissance to the end of the 19th century: succinct selections from 125 different treatises and articles, most of them unavailable elsewhere in English—Newton, Leibniz, Pascal, Riemann, Bernoulli, etc. 24 articles trace developments in the field of number, 18 cover algebra, 36 are on geometry, and 13 on calculus. Biographical-historical introductions to each article. Two volume set. Index in each. Total of 115 illustrations. Total of xxviii + 742pp. 5⅜ x 8.
S552 Vol I Paperbound **$1.85**
S553 Vol II Paperbound **$1.85**
The set, boxed **$3.50**

# CATALOGUE OF DOVER BOOKS

**\*THE THIRTEEN BOOKS OF EUCLID'S ELEMENTS, edited by T. L. Heath.** This is the complete EUCLID — the definitive edition of one of the greatest classics of the western world. Complete English translation of the Heiberg text with spurious Book XIV. Detailed 150-page introduction discusses aspects of Greek and medieval mathematics: Euclid, texts, commentators, etc. Paralleling the text is an elaborate critical exposition analyzing each definition, proposition, postulate, etc., and covering textual matters, mathematical analyses, refutations, extensions, etc. Unabridged reproduction of the Cambridge 2nd edition. 3 volumes. Total of 995 figures, 1426pp. 5⅜ x 8.             S88, 89, 90 — 3 vol. set, Paperbound **$6.00**

**\*THE GEOMETRY OF RENE DESCARTES.** The great work which founded analytic geometry. The renowned Smith-Latham translation faced with the original French text containing all of Descartes' own diagrams! Contains: Problems the Construction of Which Requires Only Straight Lines and Circles; On the Nature of Curved Lines; On the Construction of Solid or Supersolid Problems. Notes. Diagrams. 258pp.             S68 Paperbound **$1.50**

**\*A PHILOSOPHICAL ESSAY ON PROBABILITIES, P. Laplace.** Without recourse to any mathematics above grammar school, Laplace develops a philosophically, mathematically and historically classical exposition of the nature of probability: its functions and limitations, operations in practical affairs, calculations in games of chance, insurance, government, astronomy, and countless other fields. New introduction by E. T. Bell. viii + 196pp.  S166 Paperbound **$1.35**

**DE RE METALLICA, Georgius Agricola.** Written over 400 years ago, for 200 years the most authoritative first-hand account of the production of metals, translated in 1912 by former President Herbert Hoover and his wife, and today still one of the most beautiful and fascinating volumes ever produced in the history of science! 12 books, exhaustively annotated, give a wonderfully lucid and vivid picture of the history of mining, selection of sites, types of deposits, excavating pits, sinking shafts, ventilating, pumps, crushing machinery, assaying, smelting, refining metals, making salt, alum, nitre, glass, and many other topics. This definitive edition contains all 289 of the 16th century woodcuts which made the original an artistic masterpiece. It makes a superb gift for geologists, engineers, libraries, artists, historians, and everyone interested in science and early illustrative art. Biographical, historical introductions. Bibliography, survey of ancient authors. Indices. 289 illustrations. 672pp. 6¾ x 10¾. Deluxe library edition.             S6 Clothbound **$10.00**

**GEOGRAPHICAL ESSAYS, W. M. Davis.** Modern geography and geomorphology rest on the fundamental work of this scientist. His new concepts of earth-processes revolutionized science and his broad interpretation of the scope of geography created a deeper understanding of the interrelation of the landscape and the forces that mold it. This first inexpensive unabridged edition covers theory of geography, methods of advanced geographic teaching, descriptions of geographic areas, analyses of land-shaping processes, and much besides. Not only a factual and historical classic, it is still widely read for its reflections of modern scientific thought. Introduction. 130 figures. Index. vi + 777pp. 5⅜ x 8.
             S383 Paperbound **$2.95**

**CHARLES BABBAGE AND HIS CALCULATING ENGINES, edited by P. Morrison and E. Morrison.** Friend of Darwin, Humboldt, and Laplace, Babbage was a leading pioneer in large-scale mathematical machines and a prophetic herald of modern operational research—true father of Harvard's relay computer Mark I. His Difference Engine and Analytical Engine were the first successful machines in the field. This volume contains a valuable introduction on his life and work; major excerpts from his fascinating autobiography, revealing his eccentric and unusual personality; and extensive selections from "Babbage's Calculating Engines," a compilation of hard-to-find journal articles, both by Babbage and by such eminent contributors as the Countess of Lovelace, L. F. Menabrea, and Dionysius Lardner. 11 illustrations. Appendix of miscellaneous papers. Index. Bibliography. xxxviii + 400pp. 5⅜ x 8.             T12 Paperbound **$2.00**

**\*THE WORKS OF ARCHIMEDES WITH THE METHOD OF ARCHIMEDES, edited by T. L. Heath.** All the known works of the greatest mathematician of antiquity including the recently discovered METHOD OF ARCHIMEDES. This last is the only work we have which shows exactly how early mathematicians discovered their proofs before setting them down in their final perfection. A 186 page study by the eminent scholar Heath discusses Archimedes and the history of Greek mathematics. Bibliography. 563pp. 5⅜ x 8.             S9 Paperbound **$2.00**

# History of Science and Mathematics

**THE STUDY OF THE HISTORY OF MATHEMATICS, THE STUDY OF THE HISTORY OF SCIENCE, G. Sarton.** Two books bound as one. Each volume contains a long introduction to the methods and philosophy of each of these historical fields, covering the skills and sympathies of the historian, concepts of history of science, psychology of idea-creation, and the purpose of history of science. Prof. Sarton also provides more than 80 pages of classified bibliography. Complete and unabridged. Indexed. 10 illustrations. 188pp. 5⅜ x 8.     T240 Paperbound **$1.25**

**A HISTORY OF PHYSICS, Florian Cajori, Ph.D.** First written in 1899, thoroughly revised in 1929, this is still best entry into antecedents of modern theories. Precise non-mathematical discussion of ideas, theories, techniques, apparatus of each period from Greeks to 1920's, analyzing within each period basic topics of matter, mechanics, light, electricity and magnetism, sound, atomic theory, etc. Stress on modern developments, from early 19th century to present. Written with critical eye on historical development, significance. Provides most of needed historical background for student of physics. Reprint of second (1929) edition. Index. Bibliography in footnotes. 16 figures. xv + 424pp. 5⅜ x 8.     T970 Paperbound **$2.00**

**A HISTORY OF ASTRONOMY FROM THALES TO KEPLER, J. L. E. Dreyer.** Formerly titled A HISTORY OF PLANETARY SYSTEMS FROM THALES TO KEPLER. This is the only work in English which provides a detailed history of man's cosmological views from prehistoric times up through the Renaissance. It covers Egypt, Babylonia, early Greece, Alexandria, the Middle Ages, Copernicus, Tycho Brahe, Kepler, and many others. Epicycles and other complex theories of positional astronomy are explained in terms nearly everyone will find clear and easy to understand. "Standard reference on Greek astronomy and the Copernican revolution," SKY AND TELESCOPE. Bibliography. 21 diagrams. Index. xvii + 430pp. 5⅜ x 8.     S79 Paperbound **$1.98**

**A SHORT HISTORY OF ASTRONOMY, A. Berry.** A popular standard work for over 50 years, this thorough and accurate volume covers the science from primitive times to the end of the 19th century. After the Greeks and Middle Ages, individual chapters analyze Copernicus, Brahe, Galileo, Kepler, and Newton, and the mixed reception of their startling discoveries. Post-Newtonian achievements are then discussed in unusual detail: Halley, Bradley, Lagrange, Laplace, Herschel, Bessel, etc. 2 indexes. 104 illustrations, 9 portraits. xxxi + 440pp. 5⅜ x 8.
T210 Paperbound **$2.00**

**PIONEERS OF SCIENCE, Sir Oliver Lodge.** An authoritative, yet elementary history of science by a leading scientist and expositor. Concentrating on individuals—Copernicus, Brahe, Kepler, Galileo, Descartes, Newton, Laplace, Herschel, Lord Kelvin, and other scientists—the author presents their discoveries in historical order, adding biographical material on each man and full, specific explanations of their achievements. The full, clear discussions of the accomplishments of post-Newtonian astronomers are features seldom found in other books on the subject. Index. 120 illustrations. xv + 404pp. 5⅜ x 8.     T716 Paperbound **$1.65**

**THE BIRTH AND DEVELOPMENT OF THE GEOLOGICAL SCIENCES, F. D. Adams.** The most complete and thorough history of the earth sciences in print. Geological thought from earliest recorded times to the end of the 19th century—covers over 300 early thinkers and systems: fossils and hypothetical explanations of them, vulcanists vs. neptunists, figured stones and paleontology, generation of stones, and similar topics. 91 illustrations, including medieval, renaissance woodcuts, etc. 632 footnotes and bibliographic notes. Index. 511pp. 5⅜ x 8.
T5 Paperbound **$2.00**

**THE STORY OF ALCHEMY AND EARLY CHEMISTRY, J. M. Stillman.** "Add the blood of a red-haired man"—a recipe typical of the many quoted in this authoritative and readable history of the strange beliefs and practices of the alchemists. Concise studies of every leading figure in alchemy and early chemistry through Lavoisier, in this curious epic of superstition and true science, constructed from scores of rare and difficult Greek, Latin, German, and French texts. Foreword by S. W. Young. 246-item bibliography. Index. xiii + 566pp. 5⅜ x 8.
S628 Paperbound **$2.45**

**HISTORY OF MATHEMATICS, D. E. Smith.** Most comprehensive non-technical history of math in English. Discusses the lives and works of over a thousand major and minor figures, from Euclid to Descartes, Gauss, and Riemann. Vol. I: A chronological examination, from primitive concepts through Egypt, Babylonia, Greece, the Orient, Rome, the Middle Ages, the Renaissance, and up to 1900. Vol. 2: The development of ideas in specific fields and problems, up through elementary calculus. Two volumes, total of 510 illustrations, 1355pp. 5⅜ x 8. Set boxed in attractive container.     T429,430 Paperbound the set **$5.00**

# CATALOGUE OF DOVER BOOKS

**A CONCISE HISTORY OF MATHEMATICS, D. Struik.** A lucid, easily followed history of mathematical ideas and techniques from the Ancient Near East up to modern times. Requires no mathematics but will serve as an excellent introduction to mathematical concepts and great mathematicians through the method of historical development. 60 illustrations including Egyptian papyri, Greek mss., portraits of 31 eminent mathematicians. Bibliography. xix + 299pp. 5⅜ x 8. T255 Paperbound **$1.75**

**A SHORT ACCOUNT OF THE HISTORY OF MATHEMATICS, W. W. Rouse Ball.** Last previous edition (1908) hailed by mathematicians and laymen for lucid overview of math as living science, for understandable presentation of individual contributions of great mathematicians. Treats lives, discoveries of every important school and figure from Egypt, Phoenicia to late nineteenth century. Greek schools of Ionia, Cyzicus, Alexandria, Byzantium, Pythagoras; primitive arithmetic; Middle Ages and Renaissance, including European and Asiatic contributions; modern math of Descartes, Pascal, Wallis, Huygens, Newton, Euler, Lambert, Laplace, scores more. More emphasis on historical development, exposition of ideas than other books on subject. Non-technical, readable text can be followed with no more preparation than high-school algebra. Index. 544pp. 5⅜ x 8. S630 Paperbound **$2.00**

**ON MATHEMATICS AND MATHEMATICIANS, R. E. Moritz.** A ten year labor of love by the discerning and discriminating Prof. Moritz, this collection has rarely been equalled in its ability to convey the full sense of mathematics and the personalities of great mathematicians. A collection of anecdotes, aphorisms, reminiscences, philosophies, definitions, speculations, biographical insights, etc., by great mathematicians and writers: Descartes, Mill, De Morgan, Locke, Berkeley, Kant, Coleridge, Whitehead, Sylvester, Klein, and many others. Also, glimpses into the lives of mathematical giants from Archimedes to Euler, Gauss, and Weierstrass. To mathematicians, a superb book for browsing; to writers and teachers, an unequalled source of quotation; to the layman, an exciting revelation of the fullness of mathematics. Extensive cross index. 410pp. 5⅜ x 8. T489 Paperbound **$1.95**

**SIR ISAAC NEWTON: A BIOGRAPHY, Louis Trenchard More.** Standard, definitive biography of Newton, covering every phase of his life and career in its presentation of the renowned scientific genius as a living man. Objective, critical analysis of his character as well as a careful survey of his manifold accomplishments in many areas of science, and in theology, history, politics, finance. Text includes letters by Newton and acquaintances, many other papers, some translated from Latin to English by the author. Scientists, teachers of science will especially be interested in this book, which will appeal to all readers concerned with history of ideas, development of science. Republication of original (1934) edition. 1 full-page plate. Index. xii + 675pp. 5⅜ x 8½. S79 Paperbound **$2.50**

**GUIDE TO THE LITERATURE OF MATHEMATICS AND PHYSICS, N. G. Parke III.** Over 5000 entries included under approximately 120 major subject headings, of selected most important books, monographs, periodicals, articles in English, plus important works in German, French, Italian, Spanish, Russian (many recently available works). Covers every branch of physics, math, related engineering. Includes author, title, edition, publisher, place, date, number of volumes, number of pages. A 40-page introduction on the basic problems of research and study provides useful information on the organization and use of libraries, the psychology of learning, etc. This reference work will save you hours of time. 2nd revised edition. Indices of authors, subjects. 464pp. 5⅜ x 8. S447 Paperbound **$2.49**

*Dover publishes books on art, music, philosophy, literature, languages, history, social sciences, psychology, handcrafts, orientalia, puzzles and entertainments, chess, pets and gardens, books explaining science, intermediate and higher mathematics mathematical physics, engineering, biological sciences, earth sciences, classics of science, etc. Write to:*

*Dept. catrr.*
*Dover Publications, Inc.*
*180 Varick Street, N. Y. 14, N. Y.*